The Biodynamic Roots
of
Human Behavior

The Biodynamic Roots

of

Human Behavior

By

JULES H. MASSERMAN, M.D.
Professor and Co-Chairman of Psychiatry
Northwestern University Medical School
Chicago, Illinois

CHARLES C THOMAS · PUBLISHER
Springfield · Illinois · U.S.A.

Published and Distributed Throughout the World by
CHARLES C THOMAS · PUBLISHER
BANNERSTONE HOUSE
301-327 East Lawrence Avenue, Springfield, Illinois, U.S.A.
NATCHEZ PLANTATION HOUSE
735 North Atlantic Boulevard, Fort Lauderdale, Florida, U.S.A.

© *1968, by* CHARLES C THOMAS · PUBLISHER
Library of Congress Catalog Card Number: 68-13768

With THOMAS BOOKS *careful attention is given to all details of
manufacturing and design. It is the Publisher's desire to present books
that are satisfactory as to their physical qualities and artistic possibilities
and appropriate for their particular use.* THOMAS BOOKS *will be true
to those laws of quality that assure a good name and good will.*

Printed in the United States of America
H-13

PREFACE

Picture a scene some fifteen years ago in my animal laboratory in the basement of the Northwestern University Medical School. The dramatis personae consist of a psychoanalyst on a Dantesque trip to the nether regions of science, myself, and a cebus monkey named Sisyphus. The latter, some months previously, had had several unexpected encounters with a toy snake exhibited simultaneously with a conditioned food reward, and had developed persistent feeding inhibitions, multiple phobias, severe gastro-intestinal and sexual dysfunctions, peculiar stereotypies, and dereistic patterns such as eating wholly imaginary food, or maintaining a cataleptic posture for hours at a time. The monkey is silent, but the other two characters speak as follows:

Visiting Psychoanalyst (after observing the monkey somewhat disapprovingly for a few minutes): And is this what you have called an "experimental neurosis?" *I* (with polite trepidation): Well . . . operationally, yes. The phenomena you see seem to parallel in many ways those that we call neurotic or even psychotic in the human, and second, they can quite predictably be induced by controlled experimental techniques.

Psychoanalyst (patronizingly): But I can easily demonstrate that this animal does *not* have a neurosis of any kind!

I (humbly): I shall be most gratified. Please do.

Psychoanalyst (pedagogically): It's simple. All we have to do is use basic analytic concepts. Let us consider this objectively: Can a monkey know its own father?

I (reflectively): Well, deep, deep down half its DNA *is* paternal, but I don't suppose Sisyphus can ever be brought to admit it.

Psychoanalyst (patiently): You see, you are already defensive. And if this monkey never knew its own father, can it have an Oedipus complex?

[v]

I (puzzled, as usual) : But none of us—including Oedipus—
can ever really be sure who *was* his father.
Psychoanalyst (triumphantly) : *But* if you had ever been really
analyzed, you would know that even though the toy snake was
obviously a phallic threat to the monkey, in the absence of an
Oedipus complex there can be no neurosis!
I (to myself, *soto voce*) : *Non erat demonstrantum. Et non
credo, quia absurdum est.* Sisyphus moans softly.

   This scene is not a whimsical screen memory; it occurred almost literally as described, despite the fact that multiple controlled observations in field and laboratory had shown: a) that
many patterns of behavior previously thought to be exclusive human (for example, familial loyalty, altruism, dominance, peer
alliances, and so forth) could be elicited in laboratory animals
as well as observed in the feral state; b) that the dynamics of
much deviant conduct could be traced to conflicts of positive
choice or failures of adaptation under stresses that exceeded the
organism's genetic or learned capacities for adaptation; and
c) that further studies had profitably explored the rationale of
the physical, dyadic and group modalities of "therapy" that could
modify or reverse the neurotigenic process.

   It would be well if one could now say "But all doubt is past:
witness the happy event of more formal sessions in annual meet-
ings of learned biologic societies given over to Ethology and Comparative Psychology, and contemplate the numerous books
in these fields for lay as well as professional readers: Do not
these indicate that our growing recognition of its derivation
and ontology may reveal much that is basic in human behavior, even though our animal cousins have perhaps not
evolved to be as pretentious, preemptive, pompous and pug-
nacious as we have? Perhaps so, but just as medieval man
only reluctantly, and with many compromising interim formulae, gave up his geocentric cosmology despite the genius
of Copernicus, Kepler and Galileo, so also modern man, six
scores years after Darwin, can entertain the notion that per-

haps he is neither the center nor acme of all behavioral science only with resounding reservations. Among these the following are most familiar:

1. *That one must not fall into the "error of anthropomorphism,"* epitomized in Pope's "The proper study of mankind is man." But might it not well be countered: what "observation," "datum," "inference," "analysis," "theorem" or "conclusion" processed in the Kantian mind of man can be other than "anthropomorphic?" Indeed, heuristically speaking, is there a more redundant word in any language?

2. Or, *"One must not jump from animal behavior to man —they are on different evolutionary branches."* But the branches still have the same behavioral trunk and roots, and it is not irrelevant that amoebae and flatworms can, in their simple ways, not only learn unaccustomed tasks but show varying individualities and protoneurotic perversities in doing so. True, "One cannot understand the human central nervous system by studying that of the primitive amphioxus," but neither can one really understand the basic plan of all vertebrate systems, including that of man, *without* tracing certain illuminating parallels.

3. Or again, we are told that *"Animals are governed by 'instincts,' 'physiologic needs,' 'drives,' 'conditioned reflexes'"* or *other such reified* abstractions whereas, "In addition to his 'Id,' man has a unique 'Ego,' a 'Superego' a 'Social Consciousness' and 'Spiritual Aspirations'"—or other more glorified vacuities. Such polemics reveal greater expertise in evasive semantics than in phenomenologic objectivity: We invent terms that imply some supposed entity, then "explain" its postulated difference from other mystical constructs—a distinction which may actually be either nebulous or quantitative rather than qualitative—by the same convenient circularity.

4. Finally, we hear, *"But animals can't talk, and only humans can communicate what they think and feel."* Once again, not exactly so. To be disconcertingly precise, one must admit that no one can ever really know what a fellow human "thinks" or

"feels," but only what he says—and some of us expel words like a cuttlefish expells ink, to obscure our whereabouts during retreat. Nor are words themselves completely unique forms of communication: In essence, they are only the airy products of the movements of lungs, vocal chords, glottis, tongue, teeth and lips and, as every linguist knows, words reveal somewhat less of the doubly significant "postures," "attitudes" and "emotions" of the speaker than the less conscious motions of his eyes, face, arms, hands and trunk. And as men sensed long before Darwin called special attention to it, animals too have a rich repertoire of mimetics to express desires, wants, satisfactions, angers, self-assertions and deviations, whereas the higher forms have also developed a system of vocalizations which, from platypus to porpoise, may range from simple signals to considerable specificity of semantic significance. This may give pause to some overarticulate human speakers who use the same words with highly individualized, inconsistent and sometimes contradictory meanings.

This book, then, explores the comparative value (if I may use that adjective in its double sense) of feral observations and animal experimental studies in relation to their significance with regard to "normal" human conduct, its vicissitudes and variations, and the indissolubly concurrent "biological" and "psychological"—"somatopsychic," or better, *biodynamic*—rationale for treating such deviations as may be termed "neurotic" or "psychotic." With full appreciation to the preceptors remembered, the authorities cited, and the research associates that made this assembly of their work and wisdom possible, I remain, *pro tempore*.

Northwestern University   JULES H. MASSERMAN, M.D.

CONTENTS

The Biodynamic Roots
of
Human Behavior

INTRODUCTION

S<small>IGMUND</small> F<small>REUD</small>, the founder of psychoanalysis, repeatedly emphasized the importance of bioevolutionary factors in human behavior in many passages such as these:

> Important biological analogies have taught us that the psychic development of the individual is a short repetition of . . . the course of development of the race. . . . The impulses and their transformations must therefore be left to biological investigation.
> —From *Leonardo da Vinci,* pp. 71, 120

> A psychical pattern may be supposed to apply equally to the higher animals which resemble man mentally. A superego must be presumed to be present wherever, as in the case of man, there is a long period of dependence in childhood. The assumption of a distinction between ego and id in animals cannot be avoided.
> —From *Outline of Psychoanalysis,* p.17

Toward the end of his more metapsychologic speculations, Freud thus returned to the broad biological and evolutionary interests that had characterized his earlier and most productive years. And yet only a relatively few subsequent theoreticians (e.g., L. von Bertalanffy, D. Levy, D. McK. Rioch, S. Rado, R. Grinker, Sr., A. Mirsky, R. Heath, K. Pribram, A. Mandell *et al.*) remained deeply interested in what the behavioral sciences can contribute to, or receive from, the more basic disciplines of morphology and physiology, with special reference to the evolving higher neural functions and their correlations with the individual and social complexities of human conduct. Since the literature is relatively limited in this field, I shall survey the biologic data relevant to various psychoanalytic theories of fundamental import.* Let us begin by posing a few fundamental questions:

---

*As Karl Popper emphasizes in his *The Logic of Scientific Discovery*— probably the most penetrating modern work on scientific methodology—

What relationship do the "instinctive," "innate" or "unconditioned" behavior patterns of animals have to the concepts of preexperiential "primary" or "libidinal" drives or "motivations" in man?

Can the rate and order of the appearance of such patterns in young animals be correlated in any way with the postulated stages of "psychosexual maturation" in the child and adolescent? And are these phases related to metabolic processes and to the differential phylogenetic and ontogenetic development of the nervous system?

Is there determinative or presumptive evidence for the postulate of "primal aggression" or of a "death instinct?" Or may the battles over territoriality, dominance and sexual possession in both animals and man be as readily formulated according to Kropotkin's, Simpson's, Huxley's or, more recently, Montagu's concepts of a universal seeking for individual participation in an evolving social order? If so, is the ostensibly self-punitive or self-destructive behavior occasionally observed in animals (e.g., in Norwegian lemmings) based on deviant individual experiences as well as primal atavistic resonances? Or is the relatively rare occurrence of mass intraspecies warfare (as in some varieties of ants described by Schnierla) more in accord with Freud's gloomy concepts of man's thanatotropic fate?

What bearings do the ethologic concepts of "trigger-stimuli" and "social releasers" have on the early channelizations or fixa-

---

testability is the *sine qua non* of any theory. A. J. Bollet thus highlighted this criterion before the American Federation of Clinical Research *(Med Tribune,* Nov. 9, 1963, p. 12), stating that a theory is not refutable, but only that it cannot be tested by experiment. "For example, according to this criterion, Freud's psychoanalytic theory lies outside the domain of experimental science, since analysts can interpret any observations within the scope of the theory, no clinical findings really test it, or strengthen rational confidence in it. As a result adherents must accept and believe, treating Freud's theories as dogma, rather than scientific hypotheses. Freud's accomplishments, thus, have failed to lead to continued scientific progress in psychiatry. To those who disagree, may I point out that this evaluation is refutable."

tions of reaction-patterns in the human infant? In view of the relative impersonality of such early automatic responses, is every subsequent relationship in the human primarily a "transference" displacement or elaboration of such previous attachments and repulsions?

Relevant to this, of what epistemologic significance are animal studies of modes of communication, courting customs, sexual pattern and group behavior? Or studies on the experimental induction of patterns of "masochism," diffuse "aggression" and "animal neuroses?" Can the phenomena of the latter be characterized by clinical terms such as phobias, inhibitions, compulsions, regressions, symptom formations, "social maladaptations" and even "hallucinations" and "delusions?"

And, perhaps most germane of all to deviations of human behavior, can a study of the methods that may or may not be effective in relieving these symptoms in any way contribute to the understanding of clinical psychotherapy? Indeed, how readily, in contrast to lower animals, may humans be reorientated and redirected by analytic or other techniques so that they may attain a greater versatility and adaptability?

As indicated, those of us who follow a broad scientific tradition must wish to adduce evidence from every available source that might help answer such questions. I propose to survey such evidence from two special sources: first, *ethologic*—i.e., "naturalistic" observations—and second, *comparative biodynamics*—i.e., animal experimental studies.

I

BASIC CONCEPTS OF ETHOLOGY

THE KEY CONCEPTS of ethology concerned with *instinct, social releaser* and *imprinting* are generally defined as follows.

Instinct, according to a resolution of the International Ethologic Congress, refers to any mode of behavior governed by hereditary patterns of function in the central nervous system and characterized by "spontaneity . . . with modifiability through learning." *

A *social releaser* is a sensory percept that, however fragmentary in itself, is interpreted by the organism as a meaningful object and thereby furnishes an "external" fixation for "instinctive" be-

---

*Compare this with K.M. Colby's definition of an instinct as a "force" devoid of any Freudian "direction" or "aim" but consisting simply of "neutral cathexis [i.e., bindable] energy." Norbert Wiener inveighs against such formulae as follows: "One of the most abused terms in biology and psychology is that of energy. In its Aristotelian connotation, it signified the potential of action, and is not really physical, but rather a metaphysical term. Under these conditions there is perhaps some justification for using it for the tendency of an animal to follow a certain tropism or for the mind to seek a certain goal. However, it is impossible in this day and age to use the term without a strong suggestion of its physical use, and this suggestion seems to be actually intended by many of those who employ it in the science of life. In physics, energy is a quantity which represents one of the constants of integration of a certain system of ordinary differential equations. . . . In the employment of the word by Freud and by certain schools of physiologists, neither justification is present; or at the very most, no one has proved it so. There was a plethora of materialistic biological writing at the end of the last century in which the language of physics was bandied around in a very unphysical way. The same sort of quantity was now termed an energy and now a force regardless of the fact that the laws of transformation of force are widely different from those of energy. . . . It is in the line of this scientific journalese that one finds the words 'force' and 'energy' interchangeably applied to whatever it is that drives the moth into the light and the flatworm away from it. However, the moth is not pulled by the light, nor is the flatworm pushed away from it."

[6]

havior. As an example, if a red-spotted ball is exhibited above the horizontal plane to a Siamese fighting fish, the situation is apparently interpreted by the fish as an encroachment on its territory by a conspecific rival, and the ball is attacked as an intruder (N. Tinbergen). So also, the shadow of a toy plane which, moving ahead, may look vaguely like the silhouette of a flying hawk, will make new-born chicks run for cover; moving in the other direction, it apparently resembles a harmless swan and is therefore ignored.

Imprinting had been thought to be a permanent modification of behavior by a *social releaser*: e.g. Konrad Lorenz observed that if he himself squatted and quacked a few times before a brood of newly hatched ducklings, they would thenceforth follow him and ignore the mother duck whose "normal" priority was thus usurped. This definition has recently been modified so that, in recent reviews of the subject, Yasuhiko Taketomo and Eric Salzen (in Masserman, 1967) conclude that "imprinted patterns" are not eternally fixed but, like other "neuronal models," subject to later modification. However, the importance of early determinative experiences *at optimum early periods* was highlighted by Riesen, who observed that if baby chimpanzees are blindfolded for from three to six months after birth, they are apparently kept from taking advantage of that phase of cortical development best suited for the acquisition of visual perceptions; consequently, when the blindfold is removed, they can no longer "learn to see" or to recognize objects, and may even make themselves physically amaurotic by staring wide-eyed and uncomprehendingly at the sun. Hess (*v.i.*) has determined within a few hours the period within which imprinting is effective.

Such ethologic observations may be directly relevant to the permanent effects of properly timed or omitted childhood experiences during various phases of early development (*v.i.*). As an example of the highly deleterious effects of omitting such essential impressions, Bowlby has contended that if a child does not receive warm maternal care in the first three years of life he can neither appreciate nor seek friendly relationships with anyone thereafter, and thereby becomes permanently "autistic" and "schizophrenic." But since parallel lines of thinking in ethology and analytic dynamics may never meet, the following paragraphs will attempt to build bridges between them.

II

COMPARATIVE NEUROANATOMY
AND NEUROPHYSIOLOGY

Historically, Herophilus taught that the third ventricle was the "seat of the soul;" Hippocrates and later Galen believed in "elemental humors;" and Gall fostered the motion, still pursued today, that distinct "organs" or "centers" of the brain mediate percepts (Angyal, Higgins), memory (Penfield), instincts (Ostow), emotions (Arnold) or foresight (Halstead). Despite trenchant critiques by Stanley Cobb, Percival Bailey, D. McK. Rioch, Ralph Gerard *et al.*, such simple topographic concepts are not easily relinquished. As but one example, there was considerable resistance to my own early demonstration that, whereas the hypothalamus undoubtedly recruited and coordinated efferent sympathetic impulses, it could in no other sense be regarded as a "center of emotion"—an inference later confirmed by Roberts, Delgado, Jacobsen *et al.* Nevertheless, Olds, Deutsch and Brady, among others, using operant self-stimulation through implanted cerebral electrodes, have recently charted "pleasure regions" in the rhinencephalon and anterior central gray of rats, cats and monkeys, as contrasted with "avoidance reactions" elicited from the midbrain and adjacent parts of the thalamus. Heath, with similar methods in humans, found that electrical stimulation of the septal region yielded an indefinably pleasant effect, possibly because of a locally secreted "septin." The close neurophysiologic association between sexuality and sustenance postulated in psychoanalytic theory (Masserman, 1965) and the relationship of both to aggression has also been attested by McLean (1962) as follows:

Centers for sexual, oral, and aggressive functions are in close juxtaposition in various structures of the limbic system of the brain of the squirrel monkey. This approximation indicates an evolution of sexual development well above the level of the hypothalamus and may help to explain primitive mammalian interplay of oral, aggressive, and sexual behavior.

Electrode exploration of the monkey brain shows that excitation from the oral region spills readily into others concerned with genital function, while penile erection occurs as a rebound phenomenon after stimulation of a region for aggression. Assuming erection to be an indication that a structure is implicated in sexual behavior, positive loci in the forebrain and diencephalon are found along parts of 3 corticosubcortical subdivisions of the limbic system: 1) apparently coincident with the distribution of known hippocampal projections to parts of the septum, anterior thalamus, and hypothalamus; 2) in parts of the Papez circuit, comprising the mammillary bodies, mammillothalamic tract, anterior thalamic nuclei, and anterior cingulate gyrus; and 3) in parts of the medial orbital gyrus, the medial part of the medial dorsal nucleus of the thalamus, and regions of known connection between the structures.

Such observations are complicated by the fact that electrical stimulation of the same cerebral locus can produce either accentuation or inhibition of patterned behavior, depending on the form of the stimulating current, the past experiences of the organism, the immediately preceding or concurrent central or peripheral configuration of stimuli and many other factors (Masserman and Pechtel, 1956; N. Miller, 1957). The same contingencies influence the results of ablations; for example, other work in our laboratory has shown that lesions of the dorsomedial thalamic nuclei impaired previously learned skills in normal cats without greatly changing their affective reactions, whereas the same lesions markedly lowered the threshold of rage responses in cats that had been made experimentally neurotic. Amygdaloid, ventromedial thalamic and (less so) cingulate lesions mitigated neurotic behavior in adult animals, but produced severe disturbances of exploratory, feeding and sexual conduct of the young; however, neonate macaques were remarkably little affected in their physical and social development by bilateral parietocortical ablations, provided that the young monkeys were then raised in a secure and stimulating milieu. This observation, of potentially profound pediatric-psychiatric significance, has been confirmed in a clinical study by J. Arbit and G. Yacorzynski, which demonstrated that optimal child rearing could in large part prevent behavioral defects in premature or brain-injured neonates.

In a neurophysiologic-topologic approach to affect, Papez (1937) proposed his famous "mechanism of emotion" which involved recruiting pathways through the hippocampus, fornix, mammillary bodies, bundle of Vicq d'Azyr, thalamus, cingulates, and amygdalae. This circuit has more recently been elaborated by P. McLean, W. Malamud, *et al.*, to include actuating fibers from the midbrain reticular nuclei of Bechterew and Gudden, elaboration of distance-receptors signalling food or danger through the longitudinal striae from the septal region, sexuality by connections with the cuneus, and pathways via the laminary nuclei to the cortex for mnemonic storage, "symbolic" attribution and operational processing.

The functions of these neural nodes and networks, however, change continuously with current motivations and additive feedbacks. To cite but two examples, Neal Miller noted that rats will press bars to actuate electrodes inserted in the median forebrain bundle at a tempo increasing to a quasi-orgiastic peak and then promptly rotate a wheel to turn the stimulus off, indicating that the same nerve center seemed to mediate increasingly "pleasant" and then suddenly "unpleasant" drive potentials. In later studies (1965) Miller also observed that various chemicals will activate different neurophysiologic systems running through the same diencephalic locus and so produce almost opposite behavior effects. Again to illustrate the interplay of neurohormonal and experiential influences, D. S. Lehrman demonstrated that the endocrine cycles that regulate the sexual organs and activities of the ringdove are themselves exquisitely sensitive to the courting activities of the mate.* From such observations, David McK. Rioch concluded "The feelings of 'euphoria' and 'dysphoria' are

---

*The special neurophysiology of sex will be discussed in a later section.

apparently related to adequacy of CNS functioning in the interaction of the organism with the environment, rather than to
activity in any localized area."

Two questions, then, remain: In view of the rich templating
of millions of years of organismic experience in the desoxyribo-
nucleic helices in every gene, and the complex neural networks
and sensitive cybernetic feedbacks from environmental configurations that continuously affect all behavior, can one really postulate simple conative entities called "drives" or "instincts?" And,
if motivation, adaptation, maturation and retained learning are
thus indistinguishable, what becomes of our artificial "localiza-
tions" and quasi-mythologic distinctions between the "conscious"
and the "unconscious" or the "id," "ego" and "super-ego" of
the human "psyche?"*

The Neurophysiology of Experience

Himwich has pointed out that the "thymencephalon" (roughly,
the Papez circuit) is the chief repository of the biogenic amines
of the brain: acetylcholine, the indolamines including serotonin
and the catecholamines (chiefly noradrenaline and dopamine),
and that these hormones may also mediate the action of MAO
inhibitors and other "psychotropic" drugs on normal and deviant behavior. E. B. John has proposed that external sensory
stimulation may produce "dominant cerebral foci" with locally
increased free potassium and acetylcholine in various cerebral
regions as previously reported by Ukhtomski; these foci then
modify current or subsequent conditional responses (Rusinov)
through subcortical connections (since only cortical undercut-

---

*Tolman writes, "If psychology would only be content with the lower
animals, and preferably with rats, and not try to mess around with human
beings, this whole question of consciousness and of idea may well have
been omitted. But human beings insist on being included in any psychological purview. And they insist that they are conscious and do have ideas—
however improbable this latter may often appear. . . . It is in the moment
of changing behavior, in the moments of learning, that consciousness will
appear."

tings abolish their influence) and thus give each organism its unique time-space response patterns or "character."

The literature on the biochemical accompaniments of various behavior disorders is too extensive and peripheral to summarize further; for key reviews and critiques see Cleghorn, Cope, Gibbons, Green, Kurland, Mandell, Nauta, F. L. Smith, and A. S. Wolff.

III

HEREDITY, EXPERIENCE AND BEHAVIOR

ALL LIFE was long held to be super-"natural" and therefore itself inaccessible to earthly inquiry; for example, long after Friedreich Wöhler derived urea from ammonium acetate in 1828, many chemists refused to abandon Berzelius' dictum that no compound essential to "vital" processes could ever be synthesized —an attitude reflected in our current reluctance to accept Stanley's demonstration that the crystallizable DNA of the tobacco virus can really be "alive." However, William James saw "life" in atoms, Sherrington discerned "mind" in electrons, and Teillhard du Chardin regarded "perfection of conduct" as the goal of all evolution. Modern geneticists, such as the Nobelists, H. J. Muller* and Linus Pauling, insist that physicochemical heredity plays a greater role than sociocultural environment in behavioral as well as physical abnormalities and therefore warn of the race-suicidal effects of mutations induced by nuclear fallout. Franz Kallman points out that the sibling of a schizophrenic has seventeen times, and an identical twin over one hundred times, normal chances for developing schizophrenia; so also, when one parent is psychotic, the incidence in children is about 9 per cent; when both are affected it is 53 per cent.

On the microhistologic level, the amazing strides in decoding the double helices of adenine, guanine, cytosine and thymine in the chromosomal DNA that mediates our heredity (O. W. Jones, M. Nirenberg *et al.*) has had immediate relevance to psychiatry. In a technical study (1967) Benson Ginsberg demonstrated that "discrete genes [which respectively influence decarboxylase and

---

*Muller (cf. Abelson, 1965) has proposed selective DNA matchings to improve the human race by parthenogenesis.

nucleoside triphosphate activity] affect the development of at least two identifiable neural mechanisms" which govern the highly specific reactions of mouse pups of different strains to early handling. More generally, Ginsberg (1964) surveyed the limitless vistas of heredity in animals and men in the following memorable passage:

> At the moment of fertilization [the organism] receives a distillate from each of two samples in an unbroken series of evolutionary continuity. This distillate is an organized collection of potentially immortal biomolecules, none of which has known death and each of which has undergone innumerable replications and (presumably) mutations. In organization and structure, this microscopic collection of matter in the zygote nucleus represents a sampling from the accumulated experiences of countless ages of evolution. As such, it is a finely adjusted mechanism, although its components probably represent a unique qualitative combination that has never occurred before and will never occur again.

In the human, mongolism is now attributable to an extra autosomal chromosome (21-trisomy) derived from an asymmetrical division of the ovum; Klinefelter's syndrome (postpubertal eunuchism, gynecomastia and azoospermia) is caused by an extra Y, and Turner's (pituitary dysfunction) by the loss of a sex chromosone. The absence of specific enzyme-forming genes leads to congenital phenylketonuria, galactosemia, fructosemia and failures in keto-acid or carbohydrate metabolism, all of which cause mental deficiency and early death unless the error is recognized within a few days and the infant provided with a protective diet. However, the problem is complicated by the following considerations:

1. Cytoplasm carried over in cell division reciprocally influences nuclear DNA, with which it not only interacts through the mediating RNA in its own cell (Fischberg, Commoner *et al.*) but with that of remote cells in the developing embryo (Moscona). As Huntington, Pasamanick, Ingalls, Stott, F. Kelsey and others have shown, important influences on the unborn

individual can thus be exerted by physical, pharmacologic and emotional stresses affecting the mother's pregnancy.

2. Despite decades of deriding Lamarck, we have come full circle to consider the serious possibility that post-natal influence —if still perhaps only in lower animals—can also change heredity; for example, bacteria grown in media containing the "dead" DNA of another species acquire and transmit the characteristics of that species (Horsefall), and planaria can apparently transmit learning (McConnell, *v.i.*).

3. The chromosomes of some germinal cells may also be permanently changed by gamma rays, by additions or substitutions of DNA derived from viruses as "free-floating fragments of heredity," and by other means. "Protogenetic" modifications so induced may remain latent until made manifest by cellular reactions, including neoplastic ones, to later physiochemical influences. In effect, then physio-patho-experiential stresses, acting either on a prenatally or postnatally acquired genetic vulnerability, can theoretically influence every conceivable somatopsychic as well as "psychosomatic" relationship from cancer to psychosis. As a trenchant example, Waisman and Harlow recently reported that

> Experimental phenylketonuria can be produced in infant monkeys by feeding excessive quantities of l-phenylalanine soon after birth. . . . Grand mal convulsions, observed in some children with phenylketonuria, were also observed in the experimental animals. The biochemical evidence was supported by the learning data. The observed slowness in adapting to testing procedures, or even failure to adapt, and the inadequate performance suggest an intellectual defect.

Protoplasmic Learning

Frank Brown (1959), in a fascinating discussion entitled "The rhythmic nature of animals and plants," also correlates genetic proclivities, response releasers and learning as follows:

> Beans grown in constant darkness show no rhythmic sleep movements, but a single brief light shock will start off a persisting 24-

hour rhythm. . . . Living things are sensitive to additional kinds of stimuli at energy levels so low (e.g., magnetic fields, cosmic or x-rays) that we have hitherto considered the living organism completely oblivious to them. These latter potentials may soon loom importantly in many areas of biology and medicine.

We need not here enter into the current controversies among Gelber, Jensen, A. F. Mirsky *et al.* as to whether or not unicellular organisms can be "conditioned" to feeding and avoidance responses, but it seems certain that adaptive sets can occur in the most primitive neural organizations. For example, Bharucha-Reid noted that earthworms permitted to explore a maze "at will" showed a greater facility in learning a subsequently required route to a food reward than those faced with the problem *de novo*. J. McConnell *et al.* reported that the body cells of lowly flatworms that had learned a branching maze, when ingested by untrained flatworms, imparted sufficient "cellular learning"— possibly through altered RNA and DNA—to the cannibal hosts so that the latter *and their offspring* could master the maze on first trial with significantly greater rapidity and accuracy.* So also, Szymnanski and others found little difficulty in training cockroaches, perhaps the most ancient of living insects, to reverse their "instinctive" escape from light, Schierla has shown that the ant, a much more "intelligent" (adaptable) insect, can be taught to solve mazes and remember the solutions without reinforcement for months. Boycott used a deterrent electric shock to teach octopi to avoid eating crabs marked by a white sign, and noted a) that this elicited conflictful "psychosomatic" reactions such as blanchings (*v.i.*) and b) that the retention of such learning was abolished by lesions in the animal's periesophagial brain. Indeed, self maintenance, reproduction and *an innate capacity* to conserve learning may be said to be the three essential characteristics of life.

---

*See Mishler and Coogan's intriguing inquiry "Do molecules remember?" In any case, from such observations Ewen Cameron has taken the giant stride of feeding DNA (mode of education not specified) to amnesic or senile patients.

Instinct and Experience

Sauer, in an article entitled "Celestial Navigation in Birds," eloquently describes the complexity of innate avian patterns:

> When fall comes, the little garden warbler, weighing barely three quarters of an ounce, sets off one night on an unbelievable journey. All alone, never in the collective security of a flock, it wings its solitary way southwestward over Germany, France and Spain and then swings south to its distant goal in southern Africa. It flies on unerringly, covering a hundred miles or more in a single night, never once stopping in its course, certain of its goal. In the spring it takes off again, and northward retraces its path to its nesting place in a German or Scandinavian thicket—there to give birth to a new generation of little warblers which will grow up, without being taught, with the self-same capacity to follow the same route across continents and oceans by the map of the stars.

Sauer demonstrated that his warblers navigated "instinctively" by the seasonal azimuths and declensions of the sun and the stars; however, since no two warblers ever took exactly the same compass course in either spring or autumn, their flights must also have been influenced by individual experiences.

Signals and Signification

This brings up the important issue of the demonstrably variable effects ("meanings") of seemingly "objective" external stimuli. For example, hens will eat almost twice as much from large or replenished mounds of grain as from small heaps, more from a soft as compared to a hard surface, and more when other hens are present; rats will work far less ardently for food if the lid to the food box is weighted or if they had experienced a deterrent in a similar situation. Penguins deprived of eggs may attempt to hatch rounded pieces of ice (Levick) and herring gulls will desert their own small unspectacular eggs to set on a large blue-and black-spotted china dummy, demonstrating how far awry even the relatively simple "brooding instinct" may go in response to different "releasers." Disturbances in the accustomed sequence of important external events may more seriously impair neurometabolic control: Lapen, Grooner *et al.* observed that baboons subjected to physiologically adequate but temporally irregular and unpredictable routines of care and feeding developed severe hypertension, other somatic dysfunctions and disturbances of behavior serious enough to endanger the life of the animals. The relevance of such reactions to the disrupting effects of unexpectedly delayed auditory and visual feedbacks on human behavior (K.U. Smith *et al., v.i.*) is being investigated in our laboratory; preliminary results indicate that a monkey becomes highly disturbed if its conditional vocal signal for food is released to him with an 0.2 second delay. Indeed, seemingly "moderate" stresses for which the organism is completely unprepared may produce lethal results: Curt Richter reported that, in contrast to domesticated rats accustomed to frustration and confinement, wild Norway rats experimentally handicapped by having their whiskers clipped and then further frustrated by being made to swim in a glass jar, died within fifteen minutes of cardiac distention and adrenal exhaustion.

Behavioral effects between these extremes will be further discussed in the section on neurotigenesis.

The Biodynamics of Learning

Prenatal

It must be noted that some of the studies thus far reviewed subtly but inescapably reopen the problem of the parental transmission of learning, possibly by the genetic modifications mechanisms already discussed. In 1928, Pavlov asserted that rats taught to run a maze in his laboratory gave birth to rat pups that solved the same maze with greater ease: three hundred lessons in the first generation as compared with only ten lessons in the fourth. According to Gantt, Pavlov himself later questioned these experimental results, but never denied his attraction to Lamarckism, and, thus lent himself to eager identification with Communist doctrine as having sanctioned the pseudo-scientific ideas of Michurin, Lysenko *et al.* (cf. Caspari and Marshak, 1965). However, primitive adaptations that occur so early that they may change hereditary predispositions other than through selective survival have also been noted by Beach; for example, one sub-species of female moth will always lay her eggs on hackberry leaves, but if her young are raised on apple leaves, some of them will lay on apple leaves. In a more carefully controlled study, W. R. Thompson reported that he shocked pregnant mother rats in a Skinner cage and observed that their young were later deficient in food-seeking, in spontaneous activity, and in learning to manipulate the shock lever. Christian found mild hyperplasia of the adrenal fasciculata-reticularis zone in grouped pregnant females as compared to isolated controls, indicating increased ACTH release by the pituitary. Thompson suggested that the increased emotionality of the young may have been caused by epinephrine crossing the placental barrier. These effects highlight Stieglitz' (and Otto Rank's) maxim that organisms age—and in a sense "learn"—far more in the uterus than they do after birth. Sontag, from corresponding clinical evidence, believes that the emotional life of the pregnant mother significantly affects the fetus. The perennial question, then, is again raised: Does what we learn in our Darwinian classrooms and in later life really affect the innate predilections of our children?*

The Value of Movement

Ethologic observations challenge another shibboleth cherished in classical psychoanalytic—though not in pedagogic—theory: namely, the prejudice against "acting out" as a form of learning or of solutions of inner dilemmas. For example, Eckhard Hess has observed that at an optimum time of thirteen to sixteen hours after hatching, wild mallard ducklings* can be imprinted

---

*According to Darlington's incisive analysis, Darwin in his later writing acknowledges "direction" as well as "selection" as a force in evolution.

*Hess contends that "all animals showing the phenomenon of imprinting will have a critical period which ends with the onset of fear. . . . Even in the human being one could thus theoretically place the end of maximum imprinting at about 5½ months, since observers [K.M. Bridges, R.A. Spitz, K.M. Wolf *et al.*] have placed the onset of fear at about that time."

to follow a decoy *only if they are permitted to waddle after it.*
Hess therefore concluded that "the strength of the imprinting
appeared to be dependent not on the durations of the imprinting
period but on the effort exerted by the duckling;" the young
learn by doing. But even deeply imprinted activities can be
deviated: Nikolaas Tinbergen, in his classic observations, noted
that a male stickleback fish, if threatened by a dummy rival so
near the border of its territory that it is placed in obvious conflict as to whether to fight or run, either diverts its energies into
the absurdly inappropriate busyness of building a nest, or else
literally perishes in a paretic impasse.

Motility in Human Infants

Bela Mittelman and René Spitz emphasized the importance
of free musculoskeletal activity during early childhood, since
physical restraints could have neurotigenic effects. In the education of our young we teach scientific principles most effectively through learned skills; in adult life we admonish each
other that "a sound mind requires an active body" (Greek
sanitas meant indissoluble physical and psychic health) and in
geriatrics we know that somatic desuetude accelerates senile
deterioration. And yet, in some forms of analytic psychotherapy,
we sometimes disparge zestful reexplorations as abjured "acting
out," * pretend that complex human interrelationships can be
solved by supine conversation between two people respectively
immobilized by chair and couch, and hope that somehow life
will be improved without necessarily concommitant revisitations,
relearnings and new achievements in, quite literally, the *act*uality
of living.

---

*Freud cautioned the psychoanalysts of his era against letting their patients
reexplore ("act-out") their doubts and conflicts in actual behavior until
they had acquired "insight"—a term I have elsewhere defined as that,
transiently ecstatic *folie a dieux* during which analyst and patient share
complementary illusions that are supposed to explain the latter's conduct.
In contrast, operational pedagogy contends that, through properly controlled trial and corrected error, learning occurs only when the learner can
play rather than merely talk a good game.

IV

DEVELOPMENT OF INFORMATION, SYMBOLISM AND COMMUNICATION

Modes of Communication

As Seboek points out, there seems to be an unbroken line of intraspecies and interspecies signalling at all levels of life, from the relatively simple chemical or contact transfers of infusoria, through the courtship dance of the male swordtail (which the female "understands" very well) to the complex kinesics—of which the vocal cords are only the audible part—in man. A. Moles has translated at least six of the grasshopper's strident signals from grasshopperese into English, rearranged partially as follows: 1) "Oh, how nice it would be to make love!;" 2) "I would like to make love;" 3) "You are trespassing on my territory;" 4) "She's mine;" 5) "How nice to have made love!"; 6) "It is fine; life is good." In less romantic but more directed conversation, few human speeches are as compelling as the hour-long dance, interpreted by von Fritsch and Lindauer, of a dozen scout bees who effectively convince 50,000 hivemates that it is time to leave their brethren in an overcrowded nest and swarm to a new one. But bees, too, are subject to polemic paralysis; Lindauer, in delightful paraphrase of many a disastrous session of a Committee of the Whole, reports this episode:

> I once observed a swarm that was unable to make up its mind. The choice had narrowed to two sites and the partisans (two delegations of bees that had returned to the nest after searching for new sites) kept up their competitive dance for 14 days with neither side giving in. Then they stopped and the groups proceeded to commit mass suicide. They built a new hive on the nearest available bush and froze to death the following winter.

In birds, kinesic and vocal* forms of communication are more obviously present. Morris has written an exhaustive report the dry language of which can hardly conceal the versatility with which birds, by altering the arrangement of their body feathers, can signify the subtlest changes of mood in agreeable, thwarting or "neurosis-engendering" situations. Frings and Jumber recorded on tape the cry of distress and warning emitted by a starling held upside down and shaken, then amplified the sound to 30 decibels through the loud speaker of a mobile sound truck and in three nights were able to frighten away an estimated ten thousand to twelve thousand starlings which had infested Millheim, Pennsylvania. Equally interesting was the fact that, possibly because of an odor left by the frightened starlings, few came to replace them.

Monkeys and apes are, of course, exceedingly responsive to both kinesic and auditory communication, and more sensitively dependent on individual training. For example, I. A. Mirsky observed that a monkey trained to depress a switch that prevented electroshock to itself would also do so when it observed a cagemate being shocked. Our own work on conspecific signals which evoke "altruistic" behavior will be outlined below, but as another example of more remote experiential symbolism it may be mentioned here that whenever a young rhesus in our laboratory thought another monkey was being mistreated it would fetishistically fondle a rubber glove with which it had once been nursed. Zuckerman writes as follows about more highly differentiated vocal communication among baboons in the London Zoo:

> Many characteristic vocal sounds are associated with specific social activities of baboons . . . rhythmical lip, tongue and jaw movements . . . usually accompany friendly advances between two

---

*The songs of birds are at least partially learned. Baby orioles isolated by Scott did not spontaneously acquire the characteristic lay of the oriole; instead, if given the opportunity, they copied the melody of other species. So also, sparrows caged with canaries by Conradi tried to imitate the trills and chirps of canaries instead of developing their own sparrow calls.

animals. In more direct sex activity this sound may give way to a rhythmical series of deep grunts similar to those with which the animals greet the sun. These grunts are commonly made in all states of well-being. One grunting baboon seems to stimulate several others. Another characteristic cry of the baboon is the high-pitched screech of a young animal or a female, made either in a situation of obvious danger, or in situations which to the human observer do not appear to contain any cause for fear. This cry usually attracts neighboring dominant baboons [who rush to protect the supplicant]. Sometimes adult males make a similar cry, but it is not so high-pitched and accompanies states of rage occasioned either by the attack of a more dominant animal, or by its own impotent attempts to attack a fellow. By attracting other animals, it may begin a new fight. This cry is altogether different from the far-carrying, deep-throated barks heard in the wild when the members of a troop of baboons are scattered, or when a possible enemy, for instance a man, is observed approaching. This cry, which in the wild probably effects the reunion of a scattered troop, is only rarely made in captivity. I once heard a female barking this deep call after the death and removal of her baby. It is always heard when babies are removed from the Hill [a free-roaming space] to a new cage and is then raised by many animals. For several weeks after the females were removed from the Hill to a new cage two hundred yards away they continued to call in this way and to be answered by the males they had left behind.

Wynne-Edwards, in a comprehensive review, concludes "[animals send] expressions of threat, warning, fear, pain, hunger, and, at least in the highest animals, such elemental feelings as defiance, well-being, superiority, elation, excitement, friendliness, submission, dejection and solitude [which can] be systematically analyzed." In the human, similar nonverbal elements of communication have been systematically analyzed by Peter Ostwald.

As to interspecies verbal communication, Kathy Hayes taught a baby chimp to say and referentially "mean" the word *cup,* to understand many nouns (e.g., *foot, mamma*) and verbs (e.g., *give, kiss*) and to obey—though with obvious surprise—an irrational command combining these (e.g., *kiss your foot*) the first time it was uttered; so also, John Lilly insists that dolphins can be taught meaningful human speech. At the level of everyday observation, it may be left to pet owners and fond mothers to judge how eloquently expressive the mews, whines, growls, and chatterings of squirrels, chipmunks, cats, dogs, monkeys, pre-verbal babies and semiverbal children can be, and how well they can understand and "mind" verbal and nonverbal directives when they "have a mind" to do so.

Information Underload or Disturbed Feedback

As noted, Harlow and others have demonstrated that infant monkeys raised in isolation remain seriously defective in physical, sexual, maternal and social skills unless given corrective peer experiences in their second year. Since such omissions of contact and stimulus are particularly devastating in the corresponding periods of human development, we may have another explanation of the fact that infants continuously deprived of individual love and attention may become indifferent, withdrawn and stereotyped children (the "autism" of Kanner) or avoid human contacts and develop somatic disturbances that end in serious physical and behavioral deterioration (the "protophrenia" of Bourne) unless early and intensive corrective measures are instituted. The more complex effects of sensory isolation on human adults may be briefly reviewed here as follows.

The initial explorations of Donald Hebb at McGill University were supplemented by the observations of Vernon, Shurley, Friedman and others which showed that if a normal subject is confined for from three to thirty-six hours to a dark, warm, quiet room or any other environment where stimuli are minimal or held constant, the effects—depending on the subject's personality —varied from slight anxiety through resentment, fear and rage to a quasi-psychotic state characterized by persistent depersonalization and disorientation with or without hallucinations and delusions. It is significant that the trauma in these experiments arose not from "sensory deprivation" (since buzzers could sound loudly and lights could shine brightly and continuously (Davis *et al.*), but from the subject's devastating sense of impotence in deriving meanings, retaining orientation or reestablishing human concourse and influence. It was later shown by L. J. West, G. Morris *et al.*, that deprivation of sleep or of dreaming (W. Dement) could also induce severe disturbances of orientation, thought and judgment, again possibly by impairing or distorting sensorial contacts with "external reality" alternating with necessary solipsistic escapes from it. An imbalance of sensorial input, rest and imaginal processing may thus account for a class of experiences that ranges from borderline normal to seriously disturbed: *vide* the disruptive illusions and irrational impulses that beset susceptible truck drivers on long monotonous hauls and not infrequently lead to accidents, or the "break-off point" experienced by some stratosphere pilots when, after several hours of viewless, soundless, apparently motionless flight they suddenly feel divorced from their former selves and all other earthly matters and may react with trance or panic.

Information Overload

Equally significant are the effects of the opposite extreme—a rather more common condition in this era of mushrooming cacophony and technical intrusiveness. Communications engineers equip electronic computers with automatic fuses that protect their mechanical brain from energy input above efficient tolerance, whereas our own physiologic outputs are comparatively ineffective—mainly our eyelids, our stapedius muscles or total bodily escape. Consequently, as J. G. Miller has demonstrated experimentally, when any person is required, within a given time, to perceive, process and respond to what is for him an overload of incoming information—even when the data are partially of his own making—his reactions may range from "normal" to striking paradigms of the psychotic. Briefly, the following disturbances may occur:

1. Omission of intake, as in "hysterical" disturbances of sensation and functional denials of perceived reality

2. Errors of interpretation, as in illusional or hallucinatory behavior

3. "Queueing" of input, i.e. compulsive ordering and categorization, as in obsessional thinking or forced generalization

4. Filtering of data and limitation of reaction, as in inhibited, self-constricted or stereotyped character formation

5. Multiple channelizations, with partialling and fragmentation of response, or projective delegation of action to, and dependency upon, others

6. Abandonment of the stressful milieu, analogous to affective, pharamacologic and geographic escapisms

Or, finally, total obliteration as employed by suicidal patients when, in their estimation, life's demands become overwhelming.

Distortion of Coordinates

Information received in an unaccustomed or unpredictable space-time context may also impair the self-in-milieu orientation essential to normally adaptive behavior. For example, the feedback of one's recorded voice or teletyped image with a delay of only 0.2-0.5 seconds may induce disturbances varying from transient dysmnesias, stuttering, and ataxia to persistent "neurotic" or pseudo-psychotic reactions. The studies of Lee, Fairbanks, K.U. Smith *et al.* already noted, and our own unpublished work may further clarify this factor in the etiology of conduct disorders, whether or not it produces concurrent and possibly irreversible cerebral damage as suggested by Chapman, Henkle, H. G. Wolff, *et al.*

V

THE DEVELOPMENT OF ESTHETICS
AND TOOL USING

Esthetic Behavior

THE CONTENTION HAS OFTEN been advanced that animals differ from man in two major respects: 1) that they do not enhance their power through manufactured tools, and 2) that they lack, or are not interested in, "artistic creativity." But ethologists can reply that the first of these shibboleths simply distinguishes those who refuse to believe that sand spiders use pebbles to stamp out their tunnels, that Geospizas pick cactus spines with which to dig out insect prey from the bark of trees, that chimpanzees in the wild use twigs for probes and shovels, leaves for dishes or napkins (Goodall) and sticks and stones for defense against leopards (Kortland). An interesting variant in the construction of a trap device is the modernized Iron Maiden technique used by the Arizona roadrunner: as described by Dobie, this bird builds a corral of cactus leaves or prickly cholla joints around a sleeping rattlesnake, which then either starves to death or dies of multiple puncture wounds in attempting to leave its prison of daggers. In organisms with more highly potentiated nervous systems, exploration of the physical universe, presumably with a view to its control and manipulation—i.e. a technology—may take precedence over all other motivations. Thus, in an article aptly entitled "Curiosity in Monkeys," Butler reviews the observations by Harlow, Yerkes and others to the effect that monkeys and apes, particularly young ones, would leave food and other rewards to indulge in individual and conjoint exploration and "play activities" that consisted essentially in the development

[28]

of increasing knowledge about, and control of, the physical milieu. When required to do so monkeys learn to open cage locks with keys and work for differently colored "coins" with which to secure grapes from vending machines, the "value" of the token, in terms of the number of grapes it can secure, determining the effort and ingenuity the monkey will put forth to earn it. So also apes can be taught to ice skate, to assemble complex tools, drive motorcycles, recognize numerals, write in ordinal numbers and otherwise demonstrate high intellectual capacities involving "abstract thought" (Ferster). Man alone, perhaps, takes things apart to see how they work, though this is sometimes comparable to smashing a Stradivarius violin to splinters in search of the exact site of its ethereally melodious tone.

Perversity

In another sense, however, man may be following a long tradition of covert hostility to the mechanical servant-masters about him, even though he himself may have created them. Cats and dogs, domesticated almost as long as man, accept his gadgets with less manifest rebellion (though dogs will chew their leashes, or bury them intact) whereas rats and monkeys display a lesser tolerance, well described by Kavanau as follows:

> Perhaps in partial substitution for the freedom of action enjoyed in the wild. . . . When a confined animal is exposed to arbitrary or unexpected changes in environment or regime, but is provided with the means for counter-acting these changes, it typically does so. For example, if the experimenter turns on a motor-driven activity wheel in which an animal is forced to run, but which the animal can turn off, the animal immediately and invariably turns the motor off. Conversely, if an animal is running a motor-driven wheel that it has turned on itself, and the experimenter turns the motor off, it immediately turns the motor back on. Similarly, if a light is periodically turned on by the experimenter and the animal can operate a stepping switch . . . it generally steps it fully off. If, instead, the experimenter periodically turns the light off, the animal, even though nocturnal, often steps the lights fully on. Only after weeks of this full opposition to arbitrarily imposed conditions

does the animal adapt to the regime and adjust the changed light intensity to a characteristically preferred low level, rather than merely to the opposite extreme of the imposed condition.

Thus, taken alone, the nature of a specific stimulus (or activity) is an unreliable guide for interpreting the behavior of small mammals given control over its initiation or cessation. . . . Stimuli which are rewarding or punishing in certain circumstances have the opposite effect under other conditions. The seemingly enigmatic findings on self-and non-self-initiated intracranial stimulation and on the effects of shock on learning and avoidance no longer are paradoxical when the effects of subjecting experimental animals to compulsory regimes and of greatly limiting their control over their environment are taken into account.

Living Tools

There is, however, less aversion to animated servants, especially among communal insects. That tiny plant lice are "cultivated" by garden ants has long been known, but herewith an example of a more highly developed form of interanimal husbandry:

> Mexican carpenter ants less than half an inch long which live in nests tunneled out of wood raise and protect the naked, vulnerable larvae of a rare butterfly. . . . The ants keep the caterpillars in individual burros a few inches long, and plug the entrances with pellets of earth. A few ants always stay inside to guard each precious caterpillar cow. The burrows are always close to the caterpillars' favorite food plant, a low white-flowered bush, but they may be as far as 50 feet from the ant colony.
>
> When the sun has set, the guardian ants come out of the burrow and climb into the bush. They inspect every twig and leaf, looking for marauders, especially the fierce, predatory ants that infest the pine-woods and would quickly slaughter the caterpillars. . . . About 7:30 P.M. the caterpillar is let out of its burrow. Shepherded by the carpenter ants, it climbs to the topmost leaves of the bush and starts feeding greedily. The ants climb aboard and drink its honeydew on the spot.
>
> When dangerous dawn approaches, carpenter ants swarm over the caterpillar, herd it down the bush and into the burrow. Then they crawl in beside it and pull mud pellets over the entrance.

Even when the caterpillar turns into a chrysalis, they stay on guard until is emerges as a butterfly and flutters away.*

The roots of Bacchus, too, are ethologically deep. Schultz, quoted by Katz observed that another species of ant

> . . . keeps beetles, whose secretions they lick to the point of intoxication in which they may damage their nests and give their larvae to the beetles to eat, though at other times they will fight to the death for the same larvae.

The cherished strains of yeast we keep in the vats of our breweries and distilleries lend their products to a more highly developed technology in the production, sale and consumption of intoxicating liquors, but the desired effects of human behavior are not altogether different.

Design

No human engineer confined to the raw materials available to a spider, bee or beaver can improve the plan or construction of a spider web, a beehive or a beaver dam. In the field of architecture combined with domestic decoration only one of numerous examples need be cited. The bower birds of Australia and New Guinea, as reported by A. J. Marshall, build elaborate landscapes, tunnels and maypoles out of sticks, pebbles, seashells, or other materials, paint them with berry juice or charcoal mixed with saliva, and decorate them with flowers. Others construct towers up to nine feet high with teepee-like roofs and internal chambers, and improve their environs with circular lawns that they tend carefully and embellish with golden resins, garishly-colored berries, the irridescent bodies of dead insects and fresh flowers that are replaced as they wither. The scene is thus set, as it is in human affairs for intricate routines of courtship and coitus as discussed in the following section (Sibol, Gillard, Hutchinson *et al.*).

------

*Gary Ross, Louisiana State University: *Time,* December, 1963, p. 90.

VI

SEXUALITY

Evolution

Iᶠ ᴛʜᴇ ʙᴀsɪᴄ ʙɪᴏʟᴏɢɪᴄ ᴘᴜʀᴘᴏsᴇ of sex—usually submerged in the incidental excitement—is the interchange of genes so that an organism of duplex heredity can be generated, then sex is basically present in submicroscopic viruses. Functionally, these sperm-shaped minimae of living matter insert their protein protuberances into a passively receptive cell, inject their DNA, and actuate the regenerative apparatus of their submissive hostess to reproduce more viral particles out of her own protoplasm so that the progeny can leave the mother cell to repeat the cycle. At only a slightly higher organismic level, amoebae prefer to conjugate with their own kind—although here again their parting with parthenogenesis is of small comfort, say, to a sufferer from amoebic colitis.

In multicellular animals, heterosexuality becomes universal, although never an unmixed blessing to the parties concerned. To cite a familiar example in the insect world, the female praying mantis combines her nuptial maneuvers with her bridal feast, the dubiously fortunate groom being utilized for both. The male empid spider, as a defense against his similarly voracious consort who might likewise consume him with love, presents her with flies to eat during coitus, whereas the more intelligent male of a closely related species has learned to wrap up a useless bit of leaf in yards of thread, so as to conclude his sex act before the omnivorous object of his affections gets through unwinding the attractive-looking package, finds the deception, and begins eating its perpetrator (Burton).

In mammals, this erotic-incorporative sequence varies from

species to species: Among ungulates the continued presence of the protective buck is welcomed by the female, whereas among the carnivores the males are generally driven off after stud as being untrustworthy when hungry, especially with succulent and defenseless young coming due. Monkeys and apes of both sexes protect their young, whereas paleolithic human males apparently ate them as well as their mothers (Linton, Hoebel, Greenway *et al.*). Indeed, cannibalistic societies in historic times fattened females for a dual purpose, and Marco Polo described how a Manchu war lord served him with a lovely young harem girl— roasted whole with a pomegranate in her mouth. According to Mead, Malinowski, Kardiner, *et al.*, similar synethesias of sex and sustenance have been preserved into the 1960's by various African and Australasian tribes, and furnish sound anthropologic roots for the opportunistic orality of the Congolese Simbas and the dramaturgic deglutitions depicted in Tennessee Williams' *Suddenly Last Summer.* Were we, indeed, just a bit more conscious of our semantics, we would abandon common endearments such as "honey," "luscious," "sweetie pie," or the even more specific "you look good enough to eat."

The Physiology of Sex

If psychology can be defined as physiology in action, then sexuality is again demonstrably related to nutrition. In the lower animals the same enzymes and hormones affect both, e.g., Allee has shown that a hen low in the peck order of priority will begin to dominate the roost for both food and mates after a few injections of testosterone. Neurologically, the spinal portion of the central nervous system controls fairly complex activity: As Sherrington demonstrated in 1900, a spinal dog can both feed and copulate quite efficiently, and a decerebrate bitch can conceive and deliver. Best and Taylor summarize the following striking physioanatomic correlations between olfactory-gustatory and sexual processes: 1) the mucosa covering the conchae of the nose has a cavernous structure suggestive of the erectile tissue of the penis and clitoris; 2) olfactory stimuli such as musk-based perfumes are associated with the psychic aspects of sex; 3) nasal congestion (with epistaxis) occurs in many women commonly at the time of the menses, and in both sexes at puberty; 4) changes in the nasal mucosa (swelling and reddening) are common in women during pregnancy and in monkeys during the estrus cycles; 5) stimulation of the interior of the nose in rats changes the periodicity of the estrus cycles; 6) excision of the conchae in young animals (rats) induces hypoplasia of the sex organs; 7) castration produces degenerative changes in the nasal mucosa, which are reversed by estrogen injections; and 8) atrophic rhinitis can be successfully treated by the nasal application of the follicular hormone.

At higher paleocerebral levels that fit function and futurity, more elaborate sexual seekings are, as we have seen, served by the circuits of Papez, through which *Homo sapiens* retains his mesozoic heritage from the time when his ancestors sought food and mates and avoided enemies by utilizing the most primitive of distance receptors, the sense of smell. At the hominid level these rhinencephalic functions became largely inhibitory; as Kluver and Bucy have shown, lesions of the temporal lobes, (or as Pechtel and I demonstrated more specifically, the amygdalae) render most monkeys overly tame, bulimic and hypersexed. But even in man the ancient oral-erotic appetites evoked in the olfactory archipallium still engender a maze of a) alimentary and sexual reflexes channeled through the hippocampus, thalamus, cingulum and fornix to the hypothalamus, b) more persistent hormonal influences mediated through the portal circulation of Houssay to the pituitary, and c) mnemonic and symbolic resonances in thought and imagery circuited through the cuneus and frontal cortex (Paul McLean). A. E. Fisher points out that the human cerebrum is sexually equipotential: "The male and female brain are essentially identical . . . both brains contain cells that can direct female behavior and other cells that direct male behavior." But since the functions of these genetically variable structures are further modified throughout life not only by wide ranges of individual experience and rates of development but also by accidents of trauma, infection, metabolic disorders, drug effects, and so forth, any "metapsychologic" theory that traces all human behavior solely to the overriding vicissitudes of "primal sexuality" in predetermined "libidinal phases" may be attractive in its titillating simplicity, but at the price of physiologic and biodynamic naiveté.

Sexual Techniques

At the lowest level, H. S. Jennings observed that the members of a colony or *clone* of protozoa descended from the conjugation of a single parental pair divide asexually for several months and only then become sexual; in this way the *community**** achieves a "maturity" not attained by earlier generations of individuals. However, despite the chemical control and maturation of sexual capacities in most individuals of higher species, actual sex practices must, at least in part, be learned. For example, male guppies will attempt to mate indiscriminately with all likely-looking objects in their territory until they find only female guppies to be receptive (Noble); young doves (Craig), tomcats (Wortis) and apes must also pass "through a long series of fumbling approximations that look remarkably like trial-and-error learning" (Maslow) before they achieve smooth and effective autoerotic, cross-species, homosexual or heterosexual techniques. Submissive animals of either sex may assume "feminine" coital postures toward more dominant colony mates; however, according to Lashley and others this signals a denial of hostility and an invitation to friendship rather than a Freudian equation of submissiveness with "feminine inferiority."

Wooing and Contrectation

As to more elaborate preliminaries to coitus, we may cite

---

*A community is defined by Wynne-Edwards as an organization that provides concerted ("epideictic") action among its members for mutual benefit. Compare similar "superorganismic" concepts of human societies as formulated by Spencer, Toynbee and Gerard.

some trenchant passages from Burton's illuminating book, *Animal Courtship*:

> For humans, as for animals symbolism plays a very large part.
> . . . There are in both the giving of gifts, the exhibitionism, the
> dressing-up, the bowing and curtsying, the communal interest in
> the proceedings, the rivalries, the jealousies, antagonisms—in fact,
> the whole gamut; and all so very much according to tradition and
> custom (or, as we say for animal courtship, so stereotyped). If
> man had invented all these things for himself independently of what
> had been going on in the rest of the living world for a thousand
> million years or more, then the coincidence is most remarkable
> [p. 14].
>
> The premating behavior of animals high and low [brings] us as
> near to a rule as is possible in biology: that the male may do the
> courting but the female has the whip hand [p. 122].

O. Heinforth noted that a dominant gander interrupted the
public mating of couples in his pond, and observed, "To be
scandalized by the sexual acts of others is often observed in the
animal world." Lorenz, despite his qualms about "anthropomorphism," once commented to the author, "This is not jealousy,
it is pure Puritanism."

Uxorial Relations

According to Relter, the lowly wood roach will fight to defend
its mate against any intruder into their marital chamber of rotted
wood. As to tenders of devotion in higher species, Burton writes
as follows:

> A hen robin has been known to take a crumb from an observer's
> hand, fly with it to the cock, place it at his feet, open her mouth
> and quiver her wings [like a fledgling] until he picks it up and gives
> it to her. To stand on a saucer of food and to look to her mate
> to wait on her may be automatic behavior. If so, then a good deal
> of free-will, must be automatic. . . . Male starlings often carry
> flowers into their nesting hole when the female is incubating. A
> herring gull will take a shell or a sea-pink to his brooding mate
> [p. 50].

As the species approaches domesticated man, the uxorial patterns become more specialized. According to Jane Goodall, wild chimpanzees line up for the female and never fight for mates, let alone a harem. Yerkes described the behavior of captive chimpanzees as follows:

> The behavior of each mate [with regard to feeding and other privileges] seems to change in correlation with their sexual relationships, and the female comes to claim as if it were her right what previously she had allowed the male to take, while he as if in recognition of, or in exchange for, sexual accommodation during the mating period, defers to her and unprotestingly permits her to control the food-getting situation.

A chimpanzee separated from its mate may refuse food and pine away into desuetude (Kohler).

Cultural Factors

Here, of course, we must discourse at the human level, but if we now define "psychopathology" operationally as organismic maladaptation to a stressful physiocultural milieu, we again see that erotism per se (i.e. apart from concurrent motivations such as fear, rivalry, dominance or conquest, and so forth) can play a partial role in the geneses of neurotic conflicts in man only in the relatively few societies—mostly in the Judeo-Christian tradition—which adhere, as did Heinroch's gander, to sexually repressive practices. Indeed, we need not go back to paleolithic or savage times for illustrations of how sweepingly local customs still determine what is or is not regarded as sexually "proper," "adventuresome," "idiosyncratic," "deviant" or "traumatic" at any particular time or place. As but one example, the contemporary Souno Indians of the Amazon headwaters copulate openly, but would be shamed into exile if caught eating in public. In the Islamic world,* where Omar Halebis' *Laws of Love* is considered a literary masterpiece as well as a manual of eroticas blessed of Allah, no Turk or Bedouin thinks it remiss to discuss the size of his phallus and the range and objects of his amatory

---

*See Edwardes and Masters (1963).

exploits at any time. Wrote Shayk 'Omar bin Sidi en Nefwazi
in one of the more quotable passages from his *Book of the Scented
Garden Site,*

> Praise be to Allah who has placed the Fountainhead of Man's
> Greatest Pleasures in the Natural parts of Woman, and who has
> placed the source of Woman's supreme enjoyment in the Natural
> Parts of Man.

In the modern East, Jacobus Sutor, a French army surgeon
who studied the subject closely for years, found the Hindu to be
"as lascivious as the monkey. . . . Every wife betrays her husband
whenever she . . . finds pleasure or amusement in it. . . . There
are few virgins above the age of ten, the hymenal membrane
having been stretched or worn away by the little Hindu girl's
repeated contact with brother, cousins and others." (*L'Ethnologic
du Sens Genitals,* Paris, 1935)

In storied Cathay during the T'an dynasty the Empress Wa
Hu required courtiers to perform public cunnilingus on her as a
sign of vassalage while she sat enthroned. Wong Shin-cheng, in
The Golden Lotus, put it thus,

> The world is based upon continuous interaction between the
> male and female principles; therefore one cannot say that anything
> so done is out of depravity or that any sexual passion is evil.*

The term "anything" in the above quotation is comprehensive
enough to include, as Edwards and Masters again point out
in censorable detail, nearly every conceivable variation of sexual
technique among pastoral and agrarian peoples openly practiced
throughout Africa, India, Asia, and Polynesia; indeed, in only
a few Western cultures can terms such as "polymorphous per-
verse sexuality," "carnal sin," and so forth have any deprecatory
meaning. Such considerations may have led the Sufist poet Haji!
Abdu! l-Yezdi to write,**

---

*Paraphrased from Clement Egerton, London, Routledge and Kegan
Paul.
**Quoted by Sir Richard Burton.

There is no Good, there is no Bad
These are the whims of mortal will
That works me weal, that I call good
What harms and hurts I hold ill
They change with place, they shift with race
And, in the veriest span of time
Each good was banned as Sin or Crime
Each faith is false, all Faith is true
Truth is the shattered mirror strewn
In myriad bits, while each believes
His little bit the whole to own. . . .
Thy faith, why false? My faith, why true?
Tis all the work of Mine,
Only the foolish love of self
Makes the Mine excel the Thine.**

However, in full justice to our own forebears, not everyone in the Western world has continued to jitter over Jeremiah, to pore over the platitudes of Plato (who personally preferred pederasty) or stand in awe of Aristotle and Augustine. More virile voices have also been heard in Judeo-Christian history, from doubly venerable King David who proudly served eighteen wives plus numerous concubines (and by Uriah's wife Bathsheba fathered Solomon to write his lustful song of Songs) down the ages through the concupiscent Chaucer, the boisterous Boccaccio and ribald Rabelais, to the D. H. Lawrences and Normal Mailers of modern times. But local customs can change from year to year, for example, the legalistic attitude of the U. S. Armed Forces toward "covert homosexuality" has swung from relative tolerance to paranoid furor, depending on the generals who happened to be in power in the Pentagon, intercurrent "spy" scares, and other quite accidental and often irrational influences (West and Glass, 1965), and all this despite statistical evidence that known homosexuals have not only refrained from inverse behavior but have made highly creditable records in the services (Fry and Rostow).

VII

EVOLUTION OF PARENTAL BEHAVIOR

Biodynamic Basis

Here again, endocrine, ecologic and situational influences are inextricably interrelated in governing mating, nesting and nursing behavior. For example, progesterin promotes precoital nest building in rats only when a suitable locale is available (Lorenz), whereas lactating cats given a pituitary hormone that diminishes mammary congestion will abandon their litters. Interparental acceptance requires special early association: Craig observed that wild pigeons, whatever their estrous status, can be crossbred only if the future mates from different varieties are raised together. Conversely, the progeny furnish stimuli that reciprocally influence the biochemical state of the parent: Leblond could elicit "maternal" conduct in adult mice of either sex by putting them in charge of newborn litters, whereas hormonally immature males and virgin females required close "concaveation" with baby mice for from one to four days before exhibiting responses of care and protection.

Denenberg, Ottinger, and Stephens showed that in the period between birth and weaning, the behavior of the mother toward her young modifies the offspring's later emotional behavior and body weight. Denenberg and Morton demonstrated that postweaning social interactions with other organisms of the same species affect subsequent behavior. Multiple-mothering (mother rotated between her own litter and one foster litter every twenty-four hours) caused rat pups to be more emotional in adulthood than offspring reared by a single mother (Ottinger, Denenberg, and Stephens). Ressler, working with two strains of mice reared

by foster parents, found that the behavioral differences manifested in adulthood could not necessarily be attributed to genetic
rather than environmental variation, in that different amounts
of "attention" the parents of each strain paid to the young
greatly influenced their adult behavior. Denenberg, Hudgens,
and Zarrow also showed that mice raised before weaning by
Purdue-Wistar rats had their adult behavior patterns significantly
modified.

Mating

In discussing the ethologic transition from guarded individuality to conspecific sexuality and parenthood, Lorenz writes,

> The high survival value of . . . intraspecific fighting (spacing out
> of territory, defense of offspring, selection of the fittest, etc.) has
> long been securely established by ecologists. For species in which
> common parental care necessitates the staying-together of two in-
> dividuals after copulation, and particularly in truly social species,
> it was also necessary to evolve mechanisms which prevent the
> fighting between certain individuals, without, however, otherwise
> impeding the important functions of intraspecific contention. The
> development of appeasing ceremonies ensued. The most important
> of these are those evolved by the ritualization of so-called redirected
> activities, in which aggression primarily released by and directed at
> the mate or social partner, is side-tracked and directed at the
> object. In cases in which higher ritualization has set in, these
> hostile neighbor, or, in some cases, at a purely "symbolic" substitute
> behavior mechanisms, for example, the "triumph-ceremony" of
> geese, have obtained a high degree of autonomy and form a
> supremely strong bond between the individuals taking part in it.

Infant Development

Species-specific ontogenic factors are again immediately relevant; for example, in animals as highly developed as canines,
no conditioning can occur until the eyes and ears open at three
weeks, after which, according to J. P. Scott, pups can be weaned
without leaving the Levy sucking effect (*v.i.*). In human parallel, no "conditioning" of the human infant can occur until six

weeks after birth—an observation contrary to Kleinian theory but well in accord with Rene Spitz' finding that babies do not really differentiate visual configurations such as parental faces until fully six months old.

Patterns of Care

J. A. King's account of the protected maturation of the prairie dog is applicable to many gregarious species:

> After leaving his birthplace the emergent pup meets his father and other members of the coterie and enters a pup paradise. He plays with his siblings and the other young. All the adults kiss and groom him as his mother does, and he responds to them as he does to her. He readily accepts foster mothers and may spend the night with their broods. He attempts to suckle adults indiscriminately— males as well as females. A female will submit quietly; the male gently thwarts him and grooms him instead, rolling him over on his back and running his teeth through the pup's belly fur. The pup's demands for this treatment increase as he grows. He follows the adults about, climbing on them, crawling under them, and doing everything he can to entice an adult into a grooming session. Sometimes, if he fails to win attention, he may playfully jump at them, and they may enter into the game. Only on the rarest of occasions is he rebuffed by an importuned adult; seldom is he kicked or bitten or drubbed.
>
> During these first pleasant weeks the pup may even meander into adjacent coterie territories with impunity. But as he begins to mature he wanders farther and his invasions meet with less forbearance. At first the receptions are mildly hostile, but they gradually grow more severe. Soon he comes to recognize the territorial boundaries and learns that not all prairie dogs treat him alike. At about this time he begins to originate and respond to territorial calls. When he utters them in foreign territory, the immediate reprisals soon teach him to confine them to his own territory. He learns further to associate the calls with safety and his own well-being. By this time he is more cautious when he enters strange territory, and if he is approached by a resident, he retreats to his own area. He begins to use the identification kiss to discriminate between coterie members and strangers. If his kiss is not returned by another animal in his territory, he treats it suspiciously, barks at it, runs up to smell it and then dashes off. As he grows older this behavior elaborates into the tail-spreading ritual.

By the end of the summer the young prairie dog has become mature in the behavior that is essential to the social organization of the town. His fighting is less playful and more often resembles real hostility. His associations with adults are fewer because of their emigration to other areas. When he does encounter them, he may groom them as often as they do him. He keeps within his territory against invaders, particularly those of his own age, and when older prairie dogs invade, he barks as though calling for help. He has matured now, except in sexual behavior.

Higher intelligence among more advanced species requires more varied schooling. As reported by Barbara Harrison and Colter Rule, orangutan and gorilla mothers teach their offspring how to feed, walk, climb and vocalize; older peers teach them care-seeking, care-giving, sexual amenities (e.g., "presenting" the pudendum to an older or dominant animal of either sex, according special priority to the mates and offspring of high-ranking members of the group) and other necessary social customs (Haford).

Maternal Fetishism

Scull draped a mother ape in a blanket every time her infant was given to her for breast feeding, and could later use the blanket "as a symbol for the mother . . . in weaning the infant away from her." Curtis and Jean Pechtel in our laboratory studied such fetishisms in young rhesus in great detail and observed that permanent values (cathexes) were attached to toys and other objects associated with a secure infancy and early childhood, as evidenced by recourse to their proximity during periods of stress in adolescence or even late adulthood. Significantly, however, Donald Sade (in Masserman, 1967) observed that feral male rhesus monkeys almost never attempted actual coitus with their own mothers—a phenomenon placed in biocultural perspectives by Miriam Slater in the same volume.

Heterospecific Relations

Curious cross-species fixations of affection can occur between individuals and foster parents of other species. For example,

Lorenz' pet jackdaw, after "adopting" Dr. Lorenz as a somewhat overgrown substitute for one of its lost fledglings, insisted on feeding him mashed meal worms through his ear canal; at another time another self-designated foster parent, a raven, always alerted Lorenz to the approach of a supposedly mutual avian enemy with mimetic swoops and tail flips while shrieking its own pet name instead of the customary *caw!* used to warn other ravens. An orphaned baby Diana monkey raised by Leonore Brandt became exceedingly attached to her human foster mother, fed her cherished bananas, and pushed her out of open spaces into the protection of trees presumably safe from predators.

Disturbed Familial Relationships

It is again of particular significance that early familial stresses can produce serious and lasting deviations of conduct in animal as well as human progeny. For example, P. Seitz has noted that rat pups raised in large litters hoarded food more strenuously and became subject to greater handicaps in adaptation than did those from smaller and better tended litters. In a particularly striking pair of experiments, Thompson and Melzack observed that puppies raised with the best of metabolic care but without familial contacts, grew into adults subject to periods of glazed staring, apparently illusory startles, fears and rages, and peculiar attacks of epileptoid whirling; in contrast, excessively protected and petted pups (according to Thompson and Heron), grew into insecure, helpless, overdependent and jealously demanding dogs—a not uncommon development in other species. Liddell reported that kids separated from the mother ewe for only two hours remained alien to the herd the first day after birth and later developed such severe neurotic and psychosomatic handicaps that they died within six months; others separated for shorter periods in infancy survived, but bore kids whom they in turn neglected, and so perpetuated a "neurotic family history." As previously noted, Harlow's experiments with infant monkeys indicate that the "psychic traumata" involved may stem not from "oral deprivations" in the usual psychoanalytic sense (all of the young animals in these studies were well-nourished), but from the removal of opportunities for physical contact and cuddling as initiated by the infant; Harlow's baby macaques clearly cherished and avidly clung even to cruelly abusive mothers, or to artificial ones made only of wire and terry cloth, and used both as an essential source of comfort and security before undertaking new explorations.* J. Bowlby's corresponding observations in human infants, also alluded to above, are strikingly parallel: "My impression in taking the histories of many disturbed children is that there is little if any relationship between form and degree of disturbance and the extent to which the mother has permitted clinging and following, and all the behavior associated with them, or has refused them."

Regression

Relevant to such phenomena are the *fixation* of an activity that satisfies a current biologic need, or an organism's *regression* under stress to patterns of behavior previously found to be satisfactory. In relation to fixation, David Levy noted that pups adequately fed by tube or dropper but separated from the mother bitch persisted for years in nuzzling tassles, fingers or other teat substitutes. As to regression, the same author observed that a fully grown police dog which, as a puppy, had been indulgently nursed and pampered after breaking its leg, began limping again even in late adulthood whenever its master played with a child or another dog, but frisked in four-footed glee when its security seemed restored.

Population Control

In animal as in human societies, a "population explosion"

---

*Gordon Jensen and Ruth Bobbit have written an excellent review entitled "Implications of Premate Research for the Understanding of Infant Development." In *Science and Psychoanalysis,* edited by J.H. Masserman, vol. XII, 1967.

may have seriously deleterious effects on individual and group behavior. Overcrowded guppies eat their young and thus restore optimal survival density (Wynne-Edwards). Calhoun, by the simple device of forcing rat colonies to live in half their accustomed space, induced deviant sexuality, excessive fighting for food and harems, neglect of the young and cannibalism until the overcrowding was relieved; Thiessen and Rodgers attributed these effects to persistent endocrine dysfunctions consequent on excessive visual, olfactory and tactile stimuli. Corresponding patterns of infanticide with or without cannibalism in over-populated or otherwise disturbed primitive societies have been described by Malinowski and Kardiner, whereas familial abuse, abortions and child-neglect are notoriously common among crowded, underprivileged families in our own "civilized" culture.*

VIII

SOCIAL COLLABORATION

BUT EVEN SUCH seemingly biopathic patterns have race survival value, else none of us would be here to record, let alone
deplore them. Although the Darwinian phrase "survival of the
fittest" has often been misinterpreted to mean the triumph of
the most strong and savage, Simpson, Huxley, Montagu and
other paleobiologists have pointed out that survival of the individual as well as of the species has in most instances been due
to the emergence of conspecific empathy and collaboration. In
this sense, many of the patterns of group behavior most important to social psychiatry can be traced almost to their Cam-
brian roots. As an example on the unicellular level, Bonner observed that the normally free and "individualistic" myxameba,
when subjected to deprivation of food or water, congregates with
its fellows to form a migratory polycellular clone, many members
of which apparently sacrifice themselves so that others may
sporulate and live. At higher evolutionary echelons antelopes
place sentinels who remain continually on watch at the periphery
of the herd until relieved. Wounded elephants have often been
seen supported by the surrounding herd and helped to escape
to the safety of the jungle; otters, too, will rescue a wounded'
comrade (Katz). Loveridge frequently witnessed a male baboon
in flight from a predator returned to defend a wounded fellow,
or a female remain behind to protect a dead mate's body.
Schalter observed that even the awesome mountain gorilla is
"amiable and decent" to the weak and suffering of its own

---

*A current mockery is that modern anthropologists have finally discovered
the "missing link" between the lowly apes and civilized man: It is *Homo
sapiens* in his present stage of arrested development.

[47]

kind. In contrast, Zuckerman noted that baboons *kept in captivity rather than in their natural habitat* may act more like men in concentration camps, i.e. attack the weak, the ill and the aged, manhandle the females after sexual satiation, and otherwise act in a manner that would appear cruel and destructive to a human observer. Zuckerman added that under these concentration camp circumstances baboons did not seem to recognize the death of adults of their own kind. Recent work in our own laboratory on conspecific succorance indicated that midway between the above phenomena, a monkey longer accustomed to captivity may starve for days if working a lever for food also administers an electric shock to a friendly cagemate (Masserman and Wechkin, 1964); however such simian "altruism" did not extend to, or was exhibited among, laboratory cats.

There is also much ethologic evidence that if the young of different species are raised together, peaceable relations will continue into adulthood. Examples of such "cross-species friendships" may be cited as follows.

Forel let baby ants of three ordinarily hostile varieties grow up together, and observed that the adults coexisted amicably; similarly, Pattie observed that chicks raised in the company of mice later preferred them to fowl company. Kuo paired rats and kittens and reported that "kittens can be made to kill a rat, to love it, to hate it, to fear it or to play with it; it depends on the life history of the kitten." Other studies record similarly cultivated platonic companionships between a dog and vixen, and a bitch and a male fox. More bizarre friendships (Burton) have been observed between a goose and a goat, a goat and a llama, and a cat and ducklings; so also, badgers, foxes and rabbits have grown up together in mutual tolerance. Humans, too, can be accepted by feral friends: Jane Goodall, after spending months with a clan of chimpanzees in the wild, learned their language and customs so well that eventually she "was greeted almost as another chimpanzee—sometimes by a show of excitement and shaking of branches, and sometimes by a complete lack of interest." Jerome Wooley (in Masserman,

1967) reported that, by gentle gradual overtures, he could convert supposedly savage adult wolves into canine pets.

Such observations call into further question Freud's postulate of a universal "'aggressive" or "death" instinct and add important evolutionary projections to constructive elements in group and social dynamics—unfortunately, as yet far from their realization in human affairs.

Aggression and War

Is, then, organized conspecific destruction confined to *Homo sapiens?* Unfortunately not; challenges to individual combat are common throughout the animal kingdom. Burton draws their human analogies as follows:

> If a male stickleback in full breeding condition is imprisoned within a glass tube held horizontally, it will not display aggressively to a rival. As soon as the tube is held vertically, however, he will display violently. . . . A corresponding situation is seen in the case of a human being, who finds it very difficult to be aggressive sitting down. And is not our first impulse, in calming someone who is becoming aggressive, to induce him to sit down?*
>
> This is not to say that wild animals do not throw their whole being into their hostile displays and sometimes go beyond the bounds of common animal decency, especially where two contestants are equally matched in prowess and determination; but really bloody fights are rare. . . . Fundamentally, the loyalty has been primarily to the territory and only secondarily to the mate. The parallel is clear in business affairs. Wars are fought over territory; social revolutions arise from land-hungry masses; more marital difficulties spring from having to share space . . . than from any other single cause [p. 63].

The special studies of Eibl-Eibesfeldt also show that in contrast to human combat, conspecific conflicts among "lower" animals over food, territory or mates are almost never lethal. L. D. Clark, after extensive studies of the fighting behavior of "killer animals" such as *Onychomys leukogaster,* likewise concludes "aggression is not an instinct. Rage and attack are pat-

---

*Cf. also our employment of "sedative" drugs for "aggressive" patients in the section on pharmacobiodynamics.

terns of response, influenced by genetic factors but brought about by particular, threatening conditions; without the occurrence of these conditions, aggression need never occur."

Social Facilitation

In contrast to the above, Bayer noted that an apparently satiated chicken would join a companion in eating again, and Chen reported that ants worked much harder in pairs than alone. A review of many such studies led Zajone to conclude that, since "performance is facilitated [but] learning is impaired by the presence of spectators, a student should arrange to study alone, preferably in an isolated cubicle, and to take his examinations on stage in the presence of a large audience." Allport, on the basis of human data, had similarly theorized that success is fostered by "the sights and sounds of others doing the same thing." These observations may have an interesting bearing on the alternation of successive gains of insight and reorientation on solitary reflection, periodically implemented by dyadic and social interaction during clinical psychotherapy.

Animal "Warfare"

Highly socialized insects seem also to be periodically convinced that mass militancy is necessary for survival; witness this condensed account, disconcertingly human in its implications:

> Some queens invade foreign nests, kill the reigning sovereign and force her subjects to raise an alien brood that ultimately kills the natives. Red amazon ants periodically go on the warpath to capture slaves by kidnapping other larvae and pupae; these ants are completely dependent on their slaves for food, nest building, rearing and educating the broods.
>
> In the tropics, a horde of millions of legionary ants [*Eciton hamatum*] periodically advances like a terrifying dark flood, exterminating vermin, attacking reptiles and small mammals, capable of destroying pythons and suffocating a man. They bivouac in huge clusters by linking bodies and legs, yet maintain clear passageways to the queen and her brood in the center of the seething mass.

IX

EXPERIMENTAL BIODYNAMICS

Heuristics

BUT TWO QUESTIONS may still be raised: Are not these ethologic observations and inferences "subjective" and "anthropomorphized?" Also, since man alone has been regarded as capa-
ble of "higher abstractions" and the development of "mores"
and "culture," is he not the only creature subject to the individualized "psychosomatic" and social aberrations that constitute
"true" neuroses and "functional" psychoses? Such questions
are asked sufficiently frequently and sincerely to have received
extended consideration in my "Behavior and Neurosis" and related writing from 1946 to 1965, but their validity need only
briefly be reviewed here.

First, as to the pejorative use of the terms "subjective" and
"anthropomorphized," a direct epistemologic stand can be taken,
to wit: since all data, "natural" or "experimental," are simultaneously and indistinguishably "objective" and "subjective," and
since all human perceptions, memories, generalizations, abstractions, theorems, inferences, judgments, conclusions and reactions
can be molded only as human concepts or Kantian categories,
terms such as "real," "true," and "anthropomorphic" become
tautologic shibboleths, meaningless to modern science. An analogy more directly relevant to the study of comparative behavior
may be the following:

It is obvious that a man can live long and fairly happily
knowing very little about the structure and function of his central
nervous system; however, should he wish to become a neurolo-
gist, this technical information would become essential. In his
first explorations of the field it might then appear to him that

[51]

the human central nervous system is far too intricate to be profitably compared with, say, the simple neuraxis of an *Amphioxus,* and that therefore he had best confine his studies to human neuroanatomy and physiology as related to "clinical" problems. And yet, as his knowledge broadened and deepened, he would begin to appreciate that an antithetical position might be nearer the "truth;" namely, that he could not really understand the fundamental structure and function of the human central nervous system *without* studying that of the *Amphioxus,* since only then could he comprehend the basic organization (or, in quasi-eschatologic language, the "plan") common to all vertebrates in the evolutionary scale, including that of man. So also, whereas the psychiatrist and psychoanalyst obviously cannot comprehend every aspect of human conduct merely by studying mice in mazes, cats in cages or monkeys in pharmacologic hazes, such studies can, with proper criteria and controls, lead to the discovery of fundamental biodynamic principles underlying all behavior, and thus provide as many valuable leads for behavioral science and psychotherapy as does comparative neurophysiology for neurologic theory and practice.

And yet, possibly to conserve their status not only as the acme but as a unique act of creation, some men contend as a matter of precious principle that there are, after all, unbridgeable qualitative rather than quantitative differences in versatility and complexity between "animal" and "human" behavior. It is more than an *argumentum ad hominem* to note that those that hold this view are nearly always either a) animal experimentalists who nevertheless insist on publishing their studies in psychologic and psychiatric rather than in veterinary journals or b) clinicians who have never personally participated in or observed ethologic or animal experimental studies and who, incidentally, rarely like pets even when they "own" them. In contrast, it is significant that experienced psychologists and psychiatrists who have also conducted animal research (e.g., Levy, Rioch, Gantt, Seitz and others) find no difficulty in recognizing not only putative "parallelisms" but also highly illuminating evolutionary continuities in all behavior.

Principles of Biodynamics

For further elaboration and validation of these theses, the reader is referred to my more detailed discussions of our experimental studies (see bibliography); here we can do little more than state that by integrating such comparative ethologic observations with reinterpreted psychologic, social and clinical data —and then excising redundancies by the careful use of Occam's famous Razor, *essentia non sunt multiplicanda praeter necessitatem*—some of the welter of often vague and sometimes paradoxical metapsychologic theorems can be reduced to the following four operationally testable Biodynamic Principles:

Principle I: Motivation All behavior is motivated by physiologic needs in various configurations of contingency and urgency: survival, procreation and, as indicated above, esthetic creativity.

Principle II: Adaptation Every organism reacts not to an absolute "reality" but to its own interpretations of its milieu in terms of its uniquely developed capacities and experiences.

Principle III: Versatility When frustrated in pursuit of some needed satisfaction, organisms modify or substitute either their techniques or objectives, and thus maintain a necessary level of overall gratification.

Principle IV: Neurotigenesis However, when two or more urgent motivations are in sufficiently serious opposition so that the adaptive patterns required for each become mutually exclusive, the organism experiences a mounting internal tension ("anxiety"), develops increasingly severe and generalized ("symbolic") inhibitions and aversions ("phobias"), limiting ritualizations of conduct ("compulsions"), various musculo-skeletal and organic ("psychosomatic") dysfunctions, markedly deviated social interactions (self-isolation, "paranoid" suspiciousness, sexual aberrations, excessive aggression or submission) and other persistently ambivalent, ineffectively substitutive poorly adaptive ("neurotic") and/or progressively disorganized, regressive and bizarrely symbolic ("psychotic") patterns of conduct.

To most behavioral scientists and psychiatrists these principles will appear immediately relevant to human experiences, though, perhaps, no more so than other systems of integration. Let us now review various animal experimental and other data that give them greater operational significance.

Species

Any animal can, of course, be used for the study of living behavior. French, Jennings and Loeb used amoebae for basic observations of vital patterns of adaptation; McConnell, Best* et al. studied planaria; Szymanski employed cockroaches to demonstrate primitive modifications of behavior through individual experience; Pavlov and Gantt evoked more elaborate forms of learning in dogs; Liddell observed pigs and sheep; Harlow, monkeys; and Lilly, porpoises for essentially the same purposes. Similarly, Yerkes and more recently Lashley and his co-workers have confined themselves to man's embarrassingly close relative, the great apes, again with highly significant results. My collaborators and I chose rats, cats and monkeys because they are relatively easily obtained and kept, yet are instructively comparable to man in the complexity of many of their "normal" behavioral capacities and, as we shall see, in their reactions to stress and conflict.

---

*Best, in noting that even planaria have an appreciation of time and total milieu, show individuality, and may become "self-willed" and recalcitrant, commented, "Many questions are raised by these investigations. If one finds that planarian behavior resembles behavior that in higher animals one calls boredom, interest, conflict, decision, frustration, rebellion, anxiety, learning and cognitive awareness, is it permissible to say that planarians also display these attributes? The question can only be answered obliquely. All one knows of the 'mind' of another organism is inferred from its behavior and its similarity to one's own. To indicate that these behavioral programs of primitive animals may be precursors of the psychological patterns of rats, and men, one perhaps should speak of protoboredom, protointerest, protorebellion and protoanxiety."

Motivation (Principle I)

As expressed in the first Biodynamic Principle, any physiologic need can be evoked to actuate experimentally observable behavior: thirst, sexual and maternal drives, physical escape from constriction or discomfort, and so forth. These and other conations of greater or less complexity were all tested in our experiments; in practice, however, we generally utilized hunger because, though feeding behavior is itself a relatively complex expression of direct and indirect metabolic needs, it has the advantages of being easily induced, rapidly renewed and fractionally analyzable. Parenthetically, and only partially in accord with "libido" theory, it could be demonstrated (*v.i.*) that nutritive needs had deep motivational interrelationship not only with sexuality as noted in Chapter VI, but also, with patterns of gregariousness, and dominance behavior. In general, our observations were conducted as follows.

Experimental Design

Our animal subjects were placed in a glass-enclosed compartment for easy observation and photography, and trained to develop various "normal" responses and manipulative patterns to obtain specific rewards. In parallel experiments, two or more animals were placed simultaneously in such situations to elicit their interactions of "cooperation" or "hostility." Each animal was then made to contend with various obstacles and frustrations; finally, conflicts of motivation—either between equally attractive rewards or among nearly balanced attractions and aversions—were induced in order to study their etiologic and phenomenologic relationships to maladaptive and aberrant conduct. In special series of experiments these techniques were elaborated to include the effects of various drugs and of local stimulations or lesions of the central nervous system on "normal" and "neurotic" behavior. Finally, a large variety of procedures, both theoretically and empirically selected, were tested for their influence in exacerbating or ameliorating these patterns of conduct. To promote objectivity of analysis and for permanence of record, tables of data, instrumental tracings, motion picture films* and independent reports of important behavioral observations were secured in all experiments.

"Normal" Learning

In a typical experiment a dog, a cat or a monkey which had been deprived of food for from twelve to twenty-four hours was taught first to open a food box in response to a sensory signal and then to circumvent various barriers and manipulate various electrical switches or other contrivances to secure its own signals and food rewards. In such preliminary studies it was found that animals could form quite complex "symbolic" associations when appropriately motivated; for instance, cats and monkeys could be taught to "count" by pressing a series of switches in a definite order a definite number of times, differentiate between printed "signs" (German script reading *fressen* or *nicht fressen*), and distinguish single or combined odors, tones and rhythms; for that matter, the animals often anticipated the experimenter's intentions and prepared for what he was preparing to do by correctly interpreting subtle clues in his behavior of which he himself had not been aware. If the animal's perceptive, mnemonic, integrative and reactive ("intellectual") capacities were exceeded during this training period, it became recalcitrant and resistant to further learning; indeed, it would not infrequently resort to seemingly aimless play, sporadic attempts to escape or episodic, diffuse destructiveness. Certain experiments indicated that these characteristics persisted in young animals subjected to an overly intensive regimen of training which thereby permanently impaired their adaptive responses—a pedagogic tragedy exemplified clinically by the stultified genius of William Sidis, still disregarded by some teachers of our young, and almost completely ignored in psychoanalytic theory. Nearly all of our observations, on the other hand, conformed to Principle I in that no learning took place in the absence of relevant motivation, e.g., an animal that

---

*See films listed under references.

was not hungry would pay only passing notice to the food cup, whereas one trained to manipulate the signals, barriers and switches would cease to be directly interested in these paraphernalia for receiving food as soon as its hunger was satiated. Conversely, if the training remained in accord with the animal's needs and well within its capacities and temperament, it readily entered into the experimental situation, learned avidly and effectively, remained cooperative with the experimenter (except, in our experience, in the case of generally unfriendly vervet, cynamologus or adult mangabey monkeys) and was, on the whole, an active, contented, relatively tractable and thereby "well-adjusted" animal.

Adaptation Through Experience and Symbolization (Principle II)

Developmental Influences

Our studies are in accord with the generalization that the young of all organisms, including man, develop through an orderly succession of stages during which sensory modalities are distinguished, integrated concepts of the environment are developed, manipulative skills are refined, early dependencies are relinquished in favor of exploration and mastery, and peer and sexual relationships are sought through which the animal becomes normally "socialized" in its group. In continued studies over the past seven years the growth of individual animals of various species from infancy to adulthood under differing environmental influences has been carefully recorded and progressively photographed in motion pictures; these observations have revealed the following important effects on development again with significant clinical counterparts:

EARLY DEPRIVATION. Young animals subjected to periods of solitary confinement, even though otherwise physically well cared for, do not develop normal initiative, physical stamina or social relationships.

FORMATIVE EXPERIENCES. Conversely, young animals given opportunities for continuously protective and nutritive contacts with adults or peers acquire exploratory self-confidence, motor and interpersonal skills, and social "acculturations."

LEARNING. The growing infants show patterns of dependency, exploration, play, fetishism (i.e. attachment to objects representing early securities) rebelliousness, developing sexuality and other characteristics significantly parallel to those in human children. However, the surrogate-parents involved, whether or not of the animal's own species, impart their own traits to the adopted young. For example, a young rhesus raised from birth in the investigator's home learns to respond sensitively and adequately to human language and action, but may never acquire some of the patterns (e.g., a fear of snakes) "normal" to rhesus monkeys raised by their own mothers.

It will be recalled that the second biodynamic principle also states that each organism interprets and evaluates its milieu in terms of its own needs, capacities and experiences. This was particularly well-illustrated by experiments in which the animal's responses, though they seemed paradoxical to a casual observer, could nevertheless be accounted for by just such a premise. For example, monkeys who ordinarily liked bananas could be made to shun them by merely having the odor of the fruit appear during a series of frustrating situations; conversely, experiences ordinarily reacted to as unpleasant could be made paradoxically attractive by direct or indirect association with a reward. A special series of such experiments produced deviations of behavior with interesting clinical parallels as follows.

"Masochism." In these studies, cats taught to depress a switch which gave them a mild electric shock signalling the availability of food could be made eager to administer increasingly intense but apparently "symbolically substitutive" electric shocks to themselves *even after the original reward was suspended*; when the shocks so obtained became manifestly severe, their behavior would almost invariably be interpreted by observers unacquainted with

their "case histories" as a "seeking for pain" or for "self-punish-ment." This, of course, again raises the question as to whether many patterns of conduct usually interpreted as "masochistic" are essentially not an expression of the pleasure of "suffering"— a panchrestic* paradox—but are instead rooted in expectations of previously available rewards through temporarily strenuous or even hurtful behavior. If this inference proves reasonably tenable, as it certainly has in many clinical observations, it would constitute another nail in the coffin of Thanatos—the "drive toward destruction and death" postulated by Freud (1918).

Displacement: External Frustration (Principle III)

Aggression

If an animal which had become accustomed to obtaining food by manipulating electrical switches, running mazes and respond-ing to sensory signals was subsequently kept from securing its reward by some mechanical obstruction (an impassable barrier, a nonoperative switch, and so forth), its first reactions would be to expend more effort to overcome that obstacle. For ex-ample, the animal would push against the barrier, energetically work or actually jump upon the switch, try to pry open the locked food box, or use other methods of forcing a way toward its original goal. If these methods became particularly intensive (i.e. the animal would use its teeth or claws as the only tools at its command), would seem to be "attacking" its environment, yet such behavior remained on the continuum of adaptative initiative and needed no new rubric of "aggressivity" to account for its dynamics or economics.

Displacement

A further instance of this is the fact that, when more energetic efforts did not succeed in their turn, the animal did not proceed

---

*A word coined by Garrett Hardin to describe concepts so vague as to be either self-contradictory or operationally meaningless.

to annihilate the switch or food box even when it had the capacity to do so; instead, it shifted to substitutive actions or goals (Principles II and III). Cats and monkeys would press other objects in lieu of the experimental switches or try to open containers other than the foodbox, whereas dogs would generally attempt by barks and gestures to appeal to the experimenter to manipulate the recalcitrant gadgets. If these alternative patterns also proved ineffective, the animals temporarily relinquished striving for the food and instead sought other satisfactions, such as drinking excessive quantities of water, attempting to reach an animal friend or a sexual partner or playing with various objects, including their own bodies. However, most of these substitutive activities, comprising various recourses into diffusely exploratory or regressive behavior, disappeared rapidly whenever the external obstacles were removed and the animal once again found that normally adaptive patterns were effective. There was, then, no actual "extinction" of learned "conditional" responses in the Pavlovian sense; instead, in greater accord with analytic theory, such responses were merely held in abeyance ("repressed") when intercurrent experience showed they were temporarily ineffective. Consistent with this, they reappeared promptly ("return of the repressed") when the opportunity once again was offered.

Interanimal ("Social") Adaptations

Dominance and Aggression

When two animals, each of which had been trained to open a food box in response to the same signal, were placed together and the feeding signal was given to both of them, competition for the single reward was necessarily engendered. In nearly all cases the rivalry resulted in one of the animals becoming "dominant" in securing the reward whereas the other became "submissive," i.e. it adapted to its partner as an irremovable obstacle and thereafter occupied itself in other pursuits until the "dominant" animal ceased to preempt the food. Such hierarchies could be set up in groups of four or more animals so that the members of such groups, after a period of exploratory jockeying, would range themselves in a set order of precedence in feeding without recourse to mutually aggressive behavior. Indeed, close observation of their interactions indicated that the submissive animals treated those above them as more or less impervious barriers and adapted accordingly. This raises the interesting question as to whether organism A ever reacts to or even recognizes organism B except as B facilitates or blocks the current or anticipated satisfaction of A.* If, then, the interactions are deeply gratifying the relationship may be termed "love" ("mutual" if both parties can share the satisfactions) and lead to various forms of symbiosis; conversely, reciprocal attitudes of aversion or conflict—subjectively sensed as hostility or hatred—are accompanied by greater or lesser degrees of defensive or eliminative hostile action.

Collaboration and Parasitism

One pattern of conspecific "altruism" has already been described in the section on ethology, but an even more intriguing paradigm of human relationships appeared in a series of experiments specifically designed to explore such patterns more thoroughly. In these, cats were individually trained to work an electric switch that flashed a signal light and deposited a single pellet of food in the food box. Two of the animals were then placed together in the experimental apparatus with a transparent barrier between the switch and food box so arranged that the animal which tried to work the switch was itself barred from feeding, whereas the food reward became readily available to

---

*B need not actually be an "organism;" indeed, "animate" and "inanimate" objects are, as Piaget emphasized, distinguished only relatively late in life and even then only partially: a graceful sailboat or a lovely Cremona violin are as individualized and near-living creations to their ardent devotees as are inanimate terrycloth "mothers" to Harlow's baby monkeys.

its partner. Obviously, many patterns of interaction were possible under such circumstances, but the following occurred most typically: After some initial random activity and individual adjustment, both animals would discover that "cooperation" was the only way in which either would get fed, so that for a time the two alternated in working the food switch for each other. This arrangement broke down when one of the cats began to linger near the food box in order to gulp every available pellet; under such circumstances its partner, deprived of all reward, likewise refused to work the switch. The inevitable result was that each animal, in a joint caricature of a sitdown strike, remained stubbornly inactive on its own side of the barrier while both starved. Eventually, one of the animals—usually the one that had previously shown the most initiative—would make another discovery: If it worked the switch six or eight times in rapid succession and *then* hurried to the food box, it could salvage the last two or three pellets before its partner, who had waited at the box, had eaten them all. From this a unique relationship evolved: One of the pair remained a "parasite" who lived off the "worker's" toil, whereas the worker remained seemingly content to supply food for both. Finally, an even more satisfactory solution was achieved by two of the workers in this series who, in the feline world, would rank as mechanical geniuses. In what seemed to be a flash of inspiration they so wedged the switch into a corner of the cage that it operated the automatic feeder continuously and thus provided a plentitude of pellets for both animals without further effort from either—a "technological solution" in the modern mode of a previously disruptive socioeconomic problem.

Neurotigenesis: Effects of Adaptational Conflict (Principle IV)

Prior to our investigations, Pavlov, Shenger-Krestovnikova, Gantt and others had induced conflicts of adaptation by the traditional method of making the "conditioned stimuli" for positive or negative "conditioned reflexes" approach too closely to each other, i.e. a circle signalled the availability of food, but an almost circular ellipse, none; or, nearly synchronous and thereby indistinguishable metronome beats each heralded opposite events. Under such circumstances the animal, in Pavlov's words, could no longer differentiate between "positive" and "negative" stimuli and therefore became "experimentally neurotic." It may be that here Pavlov was approaching, though in his own somewhat doctrinaire fashion, perhaps the fundamental etiologic factor in all "neurotigenesis," namely, a degree of unpredictability in its milieu that seriously threatens the competence and security of an organism—a generalization that would include the devastating effects of genetic errors (Ginsberg), infantile metabolic stresses (Waismann), childhood deprivations (Harlow, Spitz, Bowlby), adult communicative isolation (Hebb) information overload (J. G. Miller), delayed feedback (K. U. Smith) and other disruptive threats to learned and ordinarily effective methods of information-processing and environmental control as reviewed above.

In our own studies, instead of converging Pavlovian "positive" and "negative" signals, we employed direct conflicts of motivation in accordance with Biodynamic Principle IV, and thus elicited aberrations of behavior that could justifiably be called more intensely, sweepingly and persistently neurotic. Significantly —and in a manner again inadequately covered by classical analytic theory—*these conflicts could be set up by opposing motivations of approximately equal strength even when both were "positive."* For example, requiring an animal to choose between equally attractive but mutually exclusive foods, or by positioning a hungry lactating (or estrous) female at a motivational point equidistant between food and an importunate litter (or male) so that one attraction balanced but precluded the other (Masserman *et al.*, 1963). In human parallel it is a clinical phenomenon of corresponding significance that severe anxieties, paralyzing ambivalence, futile compulsivities and even deep depressions can be precipitated by conflicting *positive* motivations (for example, toward mutually exclusive jobs or spouses) as well as by conflicts between "positive" and "negative" or purely "negative" ones (e.g. a difficult choice between equally dubious modes of escape from danger) an observation that supports the etiologic importance of adaptational *conflict* rather than (as Wolpe, Eysenck and others contend) fear alone in the genesis of neurotic behavior. In animals, however, such conflicts could be more easily induced between "goal-directed" conations such as hunger, thirst or sex on the one hand, as opposed to "aversive" ones, e.g. inertia, or fear of falling or injury on the other. In the latter instances a typical experiment would run as follows.

Technique of Neurotigenesis

A cat, dog or monkey which had been long accustomed to securing its food by, say, pressing a series of switches in a definite order and obtaining appropriate signals that food was available in the food box, would one day, when opening the box to receive the reward, be subjected to a traumatically deterrent stimulus. The latter need not be somatically damaging; it could take the form of any "unpleasant" physical sensation such as a harmless condenser shock or an equally benign but startling air blast across the food box. Even more effective in the case of monkeys was a completely "psychologic" trauma such as the sudden appearance of the head of a toy rubber snake in lieu of, or accompanying, the expected reward. This last phenomenon was of such great semeiologic interest that we made it an object of special study and found that, whereas animated toys or even live frogs and lizards would rarely produce aversive effects, any object that approached resemblance to a snake (for example, a rubber tube constricted near one end) became traumatic even to laboratory-born monkeys which could have had no contact with snakes of any kind, yet nevertheless seemed to have an innate fear of anything that resembled them. The relevance of such observations to Pavlov's "unconditioned reflexes" or Jung's concepts of atavistic "racial memories" is problematic.

Development of Neuroses

All animals were adversely affected by the conflictful experiences described, though the nature, intensity and duration of the aberrations of behavior induced varied with the urgency of the opposing motivations, the availability of substitutive satisfactions for, or partial solutions of, the dilemma through the use of previously learned skills and many other considerations involving the severity of the stress versus the unique vulnerability or adaptabilities of the individual animal. In general, however, the following series of events was observed when an animal was subjected to a typical conflict between hunger and fear.

First, the animal, after a preliminary startle, acted as if to deny the unwonted experience; it would work the switches once more, secure the signals and again open the food box, though now with some hesitation and a subtly changed mode of manipulation. The usual procedure was then to permit the animal to feed again, but after it had consumed several pellets it was once more subjected to the "traumatic" stimulus. Following a number of such conflictful experiences (two to seven in cats or dogs, usually more in monkeys) the animal began to develop the following patterns of aberration, so closely akin to those seen clinically that the term "experimental neurosis" could with considerable validity be applied:

Pervasive anxiety was indicated by a low threshold of startle with persistent hyperirritability, muscular tension, crouched body postures, mydriasis, and other measurable physiologic indexes such as hidrosis, irregularly accelerated pulse rate, raised blood pressure and increased coagulability and 17-ketosteroid content of the blood.

Psychosomatic symptomatology occurred in addition to these bodily changes. Many animals (though, with respect to individual "psychodynamic" as opposed to species "specificity," we could never precisely predict which and when) showed recurrent asthmatic breathing, genito-urinary dysfunctions and various gastro-intestinal disturbances such persistent anorexia, flatulence, or diarrhea of so severe a degree that food would pass almost undigested in less than an hour.

Motor defensive or mimetic reactions were likewise protean and took the following forms: inhibitions of feeding even outside the experimental apparatus to the point of self-starvation and serious cachexia; startle or phobic escape, first from stimuli directly associated with the traumatic experiences such as sensory signals (especially odors), switches, constricted spaces, and so forth, and then spreading to related situations; jerking tics of the head and body; stereotyped motor compulsions such as ritualized kneeling, sitting or turning; epileptiform seizures and, in some cases, cataleptic rigidity with partial *flexibilitas cerea.*

Sexual deviations became evident in markedly diminished heterosexual interest, accentuated homosexual activity and, especially in the case of monkeys, greatly increased direct and vicarious masturbation. One vervet, for several months after being made experimentally neurotic, spent most of his waking hours in autofellatio while completely ignoring a receptive female cagemate.

Disturbances of the sensorium were obviously more difficult to deduce, but some neurotic animals were exceedingly sensitive to even minor changes in their surroundings, whereas others showed recurrent episodes of disorientation and confusion. Some monkeys appeared to act out wishfully vivid imagery: though they refused food readily available in their food boxes, they could be observed to pick nonexistent pellets off various surfaces of the cage or from the air, then chew and swallow these fantasied tidbits with apparent relish.

Alterations in social conduct generally took the form of

inertia and withdrawal from competition, with consequent loss of position in the group hierarchy. Significantly, overt hostility toward group mates appeared only in neurotic animals which had been accustomed to dominance, but had then become neurotically inhibited from achieving direct oral, erotic or other satisfactions. Under such circumstances, they turned upon more successful rivals with displaced energy furiously wielded through tooth and claw, and be joined in this by other subdominant allies (Masserman and Marvin Woolf: *Arch. Gen. Psych.,* in press).

Regressive behavior was manifested by staid, relatively independent adult dogs or cats which, after being made neurotic, resumed many of their previously recorded puppyish or kittenish characteristics. Spider monkeys also tended to become more passively dependent and receptive of the experimenter's ministrations, but other species showed no such proclivities.

CONSTITUTIONAL INFLUENCES. Animals closest to man developed symptoms most nearly resembling those in human neuroses and psychoses, but in each case the "neurotic syndrome" induced depended less on the nature of the conflict (which could be held constant) than on the constitutional predisposition of the animal. For example, under similar stresses spider monkeys reverted to infantile dependencies or catatonic immobility; cebus developed various "psychosomatic" disturbances including functional paralyses; whereas vervets became diffusely aggressive, persisted in bizarre sexual patterns, or preferred hallucinatory satisfactions such as chewing and swallowing purely imaginary meals while avoiding real food to the point of self-starvation.

Neurotigenic Variability

Observations on one hundred forty-two cats and forty-three monkeys over a period of twelve years could be summarized as follows: Animals which fitted well into our general laboratory routine, which learned efficiently, and which explored various substitutive maneuvers in initial efforts to resolve conflictful situations subsequently showed longer continued resistance to severe stress and resumed effective behavior more readily under therapy (*v.i.*). Younger animals were more susceptible to the induction of neurosis than were older ones. There were definite species differences, i.e., spider monkeys and mangabeys were more vulnerable to our conflict-engendering procedures than were vervets and rhesus. Other factors which expedited neuroti-genesis included repetition of the traumatic experiences at unexpectedly long intervals, minimal opportunities to escape from traumata, aversive reenforcement (e.g., rubber snake with grille shock added) and a diminution of adaptive capacities produced by cerebral lesions (Pechtel and Masserman, 1956).

Neurotigenic effects in animals produced by conflictful stresses have been observed by other investigators as follows:

Hellwold noted that hens frightened by a guinea pig at food-taking time became excited, avoided the "haunted" spot because of a "fear complex" and had to be fed elsewhere after five days to prevent death from starvation.

B. Rensch taught elephants to distinguish one hundred different patterns of dots on cards that signified whether they would or would not be fed; when, however, a card pattern was equivocal and induced uncertainty and thereby conflict, the elephants attacked it and became generally dour and recalcitrant in their behavior.

Ordinarily gentle Wendy, Yerkes' favorite chimpanzee, would turn her rage on Yerkes whenever the problems he or the colony set for her would become too difficult. She would then become sullen and refractory for long periods and be preoccupied with symbolically substitutive acts. Commented Yerkes, "Sometimes it seemed as if the subject were trying to save face or deceive itself by ignoring something which is potentially dangerous, as for example, the temptation to interfere with a companion by trying to take food out of turn."

J. Brady observed that if monkeys were required to press a lever every twenty seconds for six hours to prevent shock (i.e. became what Brady calls "executive monkeys"), they died in twenty-three days of massive duodenal hemorrhages; in contrast, control monkeys, who were actually shocked but who had no lever available and were therefore in no conflict about pressing it, showed no ill effects from their experience.

Bykov and his associates in Russia condition the movements and functions of inner organs to external physical and, more significantly, social stimuli. Scull reports an extension of this work as follows: "A male and a female ape are mated, after which the male is removed to an adjacent cage and a younger, more virile male is put in with the female. The first male is obliged to look on as his former mate enjoys the affections of the interloper. The emotional strain on the deprived male produces hypertension."

P. Seitz, employing our own methods for inducing motivational conflicts as described above, produced aberrations of behavior ranging from mild phobias to intractable catalepsy. So also Jacobsen and Skaarup repeated our experiments in cats and reported that they could induce neuroses so predictably that they used numerous animals in the comparative titration of tranquilizing drugs.

X

BIODYNAMIC THERAPIES

Factors that Accentuated Neurotic Symptomatology

EXPERIMENTALLY, these were precisely those that also exacerbated the basic conflicts outlined in the previous chapter or prevented escape from them, i.e. increase in either hunger or fear, or forced transgression of the phobic, compulsive or regressive patterns described above. Under such circumstances anxiety mounted to panic, inhibitions became paralyzing and psychosomatic disturbances grew serious enough to threaten the life of the animal.

Procedures that Ameliorated Neurotic Aberrations

It would be inaccurate, of course, to state that the choice of methods selected for investigation was not influenced by the experimenter's psychiatric and psychoanalytic training and clinical experience, since certain presuppositions, consciously or not, undoubtedly remained operative. Nevertheless, various techniques of "therapy" were investigated as objectively as possible, of which the following, with brief mention of their possible clinical parallels, were found most effective.

1. SATIATION OF ONE OF THE CONFLICTFUL NEEDS. If a neurotic animal with marked inhibitions of feeding and corresponding symbolic aversions was tube-fed, its neurotic symptoms were temporarily relieved, only to recur when the necessity and the fear of spontaneous feeding returned simultaneously.

To cite a single clinical comparison, sexual intercourse may relieve repressed desire temporarily but does not usually dispel symbolically elaborated sexual conflicts and may, indeed, exacer-

abate them. It will be recalled that such observations forced
Freud to abandon his early attribution of the neuroses to quasi-
physiologic "toxic accumulations" of "repressed libido."

2. PROLONGED REST AWAY FROM THE NEUROTIGENIC SITUA-
TION. This blunted the other horn of the dilemma by removing
the animal from the original environs of conflict. It is significant
that this form of relief was minimal in monkeys in whom, as in
the case of man, neurotic reactions quickly became generalized;
moreover, animals which were returned to the laboratory even
after a year of relatively peaceful sojourn elsewhere soon rede-
veloped their neurotic patterns, even though the original traumata were not repeated.

Clinically, "rest cures" and vacations away from disturbing
situations may alleviate acute symptoms, but do not necessarily
dispel the underlying and potentially disruptive tensions. Soldiers
with "combat neuroses" may feel relieved when removed from
immediate danger but unless, as Grinker and Spiegel observed,
the original pathogenic impasse between self-preservation versus
military duty is effectively resolved, exposure to any situation
reminiscent of this conflict almost inevitably spells the reappear-
ance of neurotic reactions.

3. FORCED SOLUTION. When hunger was made maximal (from
one to three days of starvation), food was made particularly
attractive and openly available and the animal was inescapably
forced into its immediate vicinity, some neurotic animals broke
through their feeding or other inhibitions, began eating spontaneously and showed gradual relief from the various neurotic symptoms originally engendered by the hunger-fear conflict. On the
other hand, animals with lesser readaptive capacities, when
placed in similar situations calculated to shatter the motivational
impasse, reacted instead with an exacerbation of phobias and
somatic dysfunctions, destructive aggressivity or a retreat into
a quasi-cataleptic stupor.

Thus also, actively directing patients paralyzed by indecision
and anxiety into some decisive course of action is occasionally

necessary and effective, but may likewise present the danger of further bewilderment, panic or even psychotic reactions, if the readaptive capacities in space, time and modality (T. French's "ego span," or "ego strength" in other analytic terminology) are seriously exceeded.

4. SPONTANEOUS REEXPLORATION AND SOLUTION. Animals which had been trained merely to respond to an automatic food signal and which were then subjected to a counterpoised fear of feeding remained neurotic indefinitely since, without special help, they had no way of reexploring the traumatic situation. Markedly different, however, was the case of animals that had been taught to manipulate various devices that actuated the signals and feeder, since through these devices they could exert at least partial control over their environment. This stood them in crucial stead even after they were made neurotic inasmuch as, though for a time they feared almost every aspect of the apparatus, when their hunger increased they gradually made hesitant but spontaneous attempts to reexplore the operation of the switches, signals and food boxes and grew bolder and more successful as food began to reappear. If the fear-engendering situations were prematurely repeated, their effects were even more traumatizing, but if each animal's efforts were again rewarded with food as in its preneurotic experiences, it eventually became, to all appearances, as confident and effective in its behavior as ever. This, perhaps, is a paradigm of how most conflicts, and "larval neuroses," are resolved in most instances by spontaneous reexploration of the problem situation leading to the immensely reassuring discovery that something temporarily feared either does not recur, or may be mastered if it does. Pertinent also is the necessity all of us feel for acquiring a large variety of techniques to control our environment, not only for normal living but also as a means of trial reentry after retreat or flight. Explicitly, we invoke this principle in preparing our children for a wide range of contingencies; pragmatically, we employ "occupational therapy" or "job training" in our correctional institutions and hospitals to give our patients the skills,

whether major or minor, which they can later utilize to meet social challenges in the world outside. Implicitly, also, a comparable process is at work in psychoanalysis as the analyzand, in a protective, permissive situation, reexplores his conflictful and deeply repressed interpersonal desires and fantasies both verbally and through his transference relationship (*v.i.*), finds himself not punished or rejected as he had consciously or not feared he might be and thus, gaining confidence and aplomb, retransfers and "works through" his relationships and transactions with things and people in the real world about him.

5. "TRANSFERENCE" THERAPY. This leads to the question: But what about animals that had been trained to respond only to external signals and had not been taught manipulative or social skills; or if so taught, were later rendered too inhibited to use them? In such cases, it was found possible to alleviate the neurotic behavior through the more direct influence of the experimenter, who could assume the role of a reorientative trainer or "therapist." Dynamically, this influence itself was derived from the circumstance that the animal had been raised in a provident, kindly manner either in the laboratory by the experimenter himself, or elsewhere by someone who also liked animals. Indeed, if the latter were not the case, or if the animal had been subjected to adverse experiences with human beings, when it came to the laboratory the first requirement was to dispel its mistrust and recultivate its confidence; in effect, convert an initial "neutral" or "negative transference" into a "positive" one.* If, then, the animal's expectancy with regard to

---

*Whenever possible, all experimenters dissociate themselves (though such disassociation was rarely complete in the case of dependent dogs or the highly perceptive monkeys) from the animal's contacts with electroshock, the artificial snake or other traumatizing experience by having these administered either by remote control or by an automatic governor on the apparatus. Significantly, some experimenters with a basic indifference or dislike for animals were not able to secure this favorable relationship and were correspondingly unsuccessful in helping neurotic ones. In my laboratory, this was particularly true of an assistant who had himself been raised in an oriental country where cats and dogs were kept as guards or as scavengers, sometimes eaten, but almost never cherished and protected.

the experimenter, based on its transactions with him *or his surrogates,* became predominantly favorable ("positive transfer-once"), that expectancy could be utilized "therapeutically" for retraining and rehabilitation, however minimal the initial steps. For example, even the most "neurotic" animal, huddled in cata-leptic rigidity in a dark corner, might be led by gentle petting and coaxing to take food from the experimenter's hand. Once this initial receptivity was established, the animal might be en-duced to eat from the floor of the apparatus if the experimenter remained near the cage; later, it sufficed that the "therapist" was merely in the room. At any stage of this retraining the pre-mature repetition even of a faint feeding signal could repre-cipitate the conflict and disrupt the animal's recovery, perhaps irrevocably. However, if the experimenter exercised gentleness and patience and did not any time exceed the gradually regained tolerances and capacities of the animal, he could eventually induce it in successive stages to open the food box, begin again to respond to signals and manipulate switches, and to reassert its former skills and patterns of self-sustenance. The retraining could then be continued to include acceptance of previously traumatic stimuli, so that eventually the animals would welcome even an airblast or electric shock (though rarely the toy snake) as itself a harbinger of food or other rewards. After such pat-terns were in their turn reestablished, the therapist could com-plete the process by gradually withdrawing from the situation as the animal reasserted its self-sufficiency, until finally his personal ministrations or presence was no longer necessary.

To claim sweeping identities between the mechanics of these experiments and the almost incomparably more complex dynam-ics of clinical psychotherapy and psychoanalysis would be an obvious oversimplification; however, certain clinical parallels need not be overlooked. The psychotherapist, too, is preconceived as a parentally helpful surrogate, else his aid would not be sought at all. Wishfully overendowed by the patient with fantasied con-cern and competence (though often this is explicitly denied), the psychiatrist, if properly trained and experienced, modifies excessive expectations, and instead gently but effectively approaches the patient in his neurotic retreat, fills his needs personally insofar as practicable, permits him to reexplore, retest and reevaluate experiential symbols and their disruptive conflicts—first in the protected therapeutic situation, then gradually, and never more rapidly than the patient's anxiety permits—in the outside world, and finally fosters and redirects his personal relationships onto people and activities that can play a favorable and permanent role in the patient's future. This done, the therapist may relinquish his Virgilian role of guide and mentor as the patient takes his place once more in the world and no longer needs the psychiatrist personally except, perhaps, as another friend among a newfound many. Words, of course, are facile but sometimes deceptive instruments of communication, and abbreviations of statement should not contain abrogations of fact; nevertheless, perhaps it will be seen that, in a field more plagued by overobfuscation than by oversimplification, these comparisons and parallelisms are more than merely rhetorical.

6. "Social" Therapy. In some animals, the success of a sixth method dubbed, debatably but conveniently, "social" therapy or "therapy by example" indicated that one factor in the process of so-called "transference" therapy was the relatively impersonal one of making the solution of a motivational or adaptational impasse seem easier or at least possible. In this procedure, the neurotic animal was simply placed with a well-trained normal one and permitted to watch the latter work the switches and signals and then feed unharmed. After from one to several days of such observation, about half the neurotic animals would begin to approach the food box, cower less at the signals, tentatively try the switches and finally "emulate" the normal animal in resuming effective feeding patterns. Once the conflict was thus resolved, its other neurotic expressions were also in large part, but never completely, mitigated, and the animal, aside from minor residuals such as slight furtiveness, restlessness or tension, appeared to be recovered.

Though the method was simple and certainly took the least

effort on the part of the experimenter, it seems most difficult to formulate theoretically, especially since the convenient fiction of a postulated "interanimal relationship" or "identification" was dispelled when, in a control series of experiments, the neurotic animal could also be induced to resume feeding when an appropriately furred, scented and activated automaton mechanically "answered" the signals, opened the food box, revealed the presence of tempting pellets, and otherwise changed the neurotic animal's external and internal milieu.*

Perhaps, as implied previously, this is the solipsistic nidus of all "interpersonal relationships." But whatever the dynamics, we utilize such influences empirically in our clinical work: To cite but one instance, we place a neurotic child in a foster home or a special school in the hope that our young patient may be favorably influenced by the "example" of normal children being duly rewarded for patterns of behavior we wish our patient, too, to acquire. Unfortunately, psychoanalysis has long neglected group theory and practice, though these are fundamental to the development of social and community psychiatry.

Biodynamics of the Organic Therapies

Heretofore we have dealt exclusively with "psychologic" techniques of mitigating conflicts and ameliorating neurotic conduct, leaving as yet unexplored the use of drugs, electroshock, neurosurgery and other methods. The question then arises, can these, too, be brought within the purview of a comprehensive, integrative, and yet essentially dynamic approach to total behavior and to the rationale of treating its deviations? Biodynamically, the supposed hiatus between the "psychological" and "organic" approaches implied by the above question is seen to be illusory if one considers that the behavior of an organism can be defined in no other way than as its total organic functioning (though, of course, as variously perceived by others) and that

---

*Some fifteen years after such experiments in our laboratory Harlow followed this lead with his "wire and terrycloth mother-surrogates."

this functioning in turn depends first on its physiologic status as influenced by a multiplicity of structural and chemical factors (Principle I) and second, on the changes in configuration of these factors wrought by the "milieu" *as the organism perceives and reacts to its environment* (Principles II, III and IV). A priori, then, since physiochemical factors are the very basis of all function, alterations in the former can and should be employed effectively in influencing behavior—a trite statement, were we not inclined to dismiss as trite anything disconcertingly true. The point at issue may be clarified by the following experimental demonstrations.

7. PHARMACOBIODYNAMICS. As has been mentioned, we had found that many drugs employed clinically as adjuncts to psychiatric therapy (e.g., ethyl alcohol, the bromides, many of the barbiturates, and some of the opiates) had one biodynamic action in common—they dulled perception, prevented the formation of elaborate associations, and partially disorganized complex behavior patterns already formed by previous (especially recent) experiences. For instance, a dog or cat under the influence of these drugs would not react as violently to traumatic stimuli and would consequently be protected to a demonstrable degree from developing a neurosis in an experimentally controlled (but to it, a "real life") conflict- engendering situation. Thus an animal long trained to open a food box on a conditional signal would, when drugged, do so less efficiently, but neither would the same animal be as much disturbed by an airblast or electric shock concurrently administered, nor would it show seriously disruptive manifestations of conflict thereafter. Moreover, even severely neurotic animals, after being given these drugs, would apparently dissociate their recently acquired fears from their previously long-established feeding patterns, temporarily "forget" their inhibitions, phobias, compulsions and regressions and begin, however slowly or ineffectively, to work simple switch patterns to secure their food as they had done in their preneurotic state. This effect was particularly marked with alcohol; under the influence

of this drug, a neurotic animal would change when even a little drunk from a huddled, tense, frightened creature into a relatively carefree one which, though ataxic and inefficient, would amble about the apparatus working switches, flashing signals, securing its food and eating it with manifest relish. An unexpected (though, it must be confessed, delightfully significant) development in such experiments was that more than half of the neurotic animals, after being initially forced to take alcohol, experienced an apparently welcome amelioration of their necrosis and thereafter began to ingest food or drink containing alcohol to the point of self-intoxication. Moreover, this artificially induced avidity for the drug diminished markedly when the animals' neuroses were relieved, partially by their own reexplorations while intoxicated, or more effectively by the other techniques of therapy outlined above. Throughout all such experiments, however, it was again noted that the effects of alcohol and all other manipulations and medications depended not only on their specific nature, intensity and timing, but also on complex combinations of factors comprising the genetic, physical and metabolic constitution of the animal, its unique experiences, its material and social transactions during and subsequent to the procedure in question, and configurations of many other relevant influences, including the beliefs and interpretations of the observer.*

The possible clinical significance of these pharmacobiodynamic observations need not here be discussed in detail, but it may be recalled that mankind nearly always and everywhere has con-

---

*Conger and Freed have confirmed our alcohol studies in rats and Jacobsen and Smart in cats. Later studies of our own laboratory demonstrated that barbiturates and bromides were on the whole more effective in preventing or relieving neurotic reactions under controlled experimental conditions in animals than the phenothiazine compounds, reserpine derivatives of the other "antineurotics" currently being avidly promoted, despite cumulative evidence that they may produce striatal, optic, irreversible hepatic, and other damage (Bloom and Davis). One reason among others may be that neither the animals nor the experimenter were apparently much influenced by the contemporary flood of commercial literature on the "tranquilizers," "energizers," and other "miracle drugs."

cocted and consumed nepenthics (Gr. *ne-penthos*—no sorrow),
such as various volatile ethers, alcohols, marihuana, and the
opiates, to guard or release him from real and fantasied threats
of disappointment or injury. And, as noted, we prescribe sedative (sitting) or hypnotic (sleeping) drugs in measured doses
to our patients to dull their perceptions, blunt their fears and
give them temporary but welcome surcease from anxiety until
we can reach and ameliorate their underlying conflicts—a therapeutic procedure the pharmacologic aspects of which are at times
inextricable from concurrent parental-ministrative, group-partici-
pant, mysticophilic, or other connotations. Unfortunately, men
are much more likely than their animal cousins to take such
drugs to the point of addiction.

8. ELECTROSHOCK. Animals subjected to cerebral electro-
shocks corresponding in frequency and intensity with those used
in clinical therapy showed a disintegration of recently acquired
inhibitions, phobias, compulsions or other neurotic deviations and
the reemergence of earlier, simpler, more normally effective patterns. As in ancillary drug therapy, the animal's adaptations
could then be further improved by environmentally guided solutions, "transference" training and similar corrective procedures.
However, all electroshocked animals, even those subjected to
the comparatively mild unidirectional-interrupted Leduc current,
showed a permanently impaired capacity for complex learning
even when no detectable histopathologic changes in the brain
had been produced.

9. NEUROSURGERY. Obviously, any cerebral operation will
a) produce a transient general disorganization of response patterns which, like the effects of electroshock on recently acquired
neurotic deviations, may be temporarily salutary and b) result
in a circumscribed hiatus in the organism's response capacities.
Although neurosurgical studies in either animals or humans are
difficult to interpret, our work has indicated that lesions in the
ventromedial thalami or amygdalae, and less so in the cingulate
gyri, may disintegrate experimentally-induced neurotic patterns

and overbalance the corresponding organic loss in adaptive skills by a sufficiently wide margin so that from the standpoint of survival and apparent contentment, the animal is seemingly benefited. However, although there are many qualifications, one in particular may outweigh others in basic significance, namely, *that the effects of apparently identical lesions in different animals once again vary with the preceding experiences of each.* Thus, neonate animals subjected to parietal ablations compensated so remarkably well after a year of special care and training that elaborate tests of abstract learning were required to detect any remaining deficit. (Masserman and Pechtel, film on Penrod, 1961). Conversely, neurotic kittens or young monkeys subjected to bilateral amygdaloid or other lesions in the "neuro-emotional cycle" of Papez and the "visceral brain" of McLean were relieved of neurotic patterns to a far lesser extent and remained much more disorganized and diffusely erotic and "unrealistic" in their behavior than was the case with adult animals. It may here be recalled that lesions in the dorsomedial nucleus of the thalamus in normal cats impaired their acquired skills and relearning ability but rendered them relatively passive and friendly; in contrast, identical lesions in cats which had previously been made experimentally neurotic produced similar effects on learned behavior, but released unmistakable patterns of hostility and overt aggression.

This, then, was further evidence that the effects even of discrete physical traumata can be understood or treated only with reference to the functional residuls left in the entire central nervous system by the previous experiences of the organism. Obviously, great care in the interpretation of the "results of brain lesions" is necessary. Pechtel and I (1956) summarized the desirable comprehensiveness and necessary precautions in such neurophysiologic inferences as follows:

> Studies such as these must contend . . . with many . . . unknowns which can at best be only partially dealt with. Among these are
> 1) the unique genetic and experiential background of each animal;
> 2) its subtly but necessarily different handling . . . by different

experimenters, no matter how purportedly constant the procedure; 3) the impossibility of absolutely objective observation, grading, or reporting of complex behavior patterns; and 4) the surgical impracticality, in view of variability in blood supply, projection pathways, and other anatomic features, of producing exactly delimited cerebral lesions. Finally, from the standpoint of comparative neurophysiology, the troublesome question remains as to whether homologous lesions in animals can inform us accurately about functions in the human central nervous system, in which such marked encephalization and other shifts of function have occurred. Nevertheless, animal studies have once again helped to substantiate an important clinical maxim: that the permanent effects of a cerebral lesion depend perhaps less on its site or even extent than on the personality of the patient, his significant pretraumatic or preoperative experiences, and the physical and psychiatric care given him during the crucial period of rehabilitation.

Translated clinically, each person behaves differently from every other because a) he was differently constituted at birth and b) because he has had different experiences; ergo, 1) he will react uniquely to any given cerebral lesions and 2) he will need rehabilitative therapy specially tailored to fit his frame and modes of action, hide his defects, and best utilize his remaining capacities for optimal adaptation. Moreover, in human imagery, the experience of an operation or of induced convulsions or comas may have the added symbolic significance of disruptive psychologic cataclysms, of expiations of unconscious guilt, of magical survival, and of final rebirth under the welcoming aegis of a kindly and seemingly omnipotent therapist—all of profound significance in human thought and behavior.

Ethoanthropologic Significance

The preceding and countless other observations form the background for the increasing frequency of statements like the following from eminent biologists:

> For that which befalleth the sons of men befalleth beasts . . . as one dieth so dieth the other; yes, they have all one breath, so that a man hath no pre-eminence above a beast.—Ecclesiastes 2:19.
> No absolute structural line of demarcation can be drawn between

the animal world and ourselves: and I may add that the attempt to draw a psychical distinction is equally futile, and that even the highest faculties of feeling and of intellect begin to germinate in lower forms of life.—T. H. Huxley: *Man's Place in Nature,* 1898.

Whatever may have been his views at the start of his career, a biologist comes to realize after years of close study that there is no fundamental difference between himself or the rest of mankind and the living world as a whole, plant or animal.—M. Burton, 1954.

Comparisons between *Homo sapiens* and other animals are legitimate contributions to comparative psychology, and comparisons between two or more non-human species are equally admissible. Like any other responsible scientist, the comparative psychologist is concerned with the understanding of his own species and with its welfare; but his primary aim is the exposition of general laws of behavior regardless of their immediate applicability to the problems of human existence.—F.A. Beach: *The Snark was a Boojum,* 1950.

Bertrand Russell, in his *Outline of Philosophy,* is even more discerning:

All animals that have been carefully observed have behaved so as to confirm the philosophy in which the observer believed before his observation began. Nay, more, they have all displayed the national characteristics of the observer. [Animals in British laboratories somehow muddle through]. Animals studied by Americans rush about frantically with an incredible display of hustle and pep, and at last achieve the desired result by chance. Animals observed by Germans sit still and think, and at last evolve the solution out of their inner consciousness.

XI

BEYOND ETHOLOGY:
THE UR-ADAPTATIONS OF MAN

AND YET ALL THESE ontogenic, physiologic, ethologic, experimental and philosophic considerations will still seem irrelevant to those partisans of the "classical" (as distinguished from the Freudian) spirit in psychoanalysis who prefer to regard man as a special creation unique and apart whose behavior can be understood only in the terms of an almost monothetic metapsychology.* Curiously, even this limited position is of heuristic value, since it must be admitted that human behavior is vastly, though not incomparably, more versatile and elaborately transactive than that of other animals. Let us briefly survey these differences.

It has sometimes been said that there are two types of human beings—one of which presumes to believe there *are* two types of human beings. As a well-known example, C. P. Snow dichotomized all scientists according to their values—and thereby their life interests—as *either* physicomathematical *or* as humanists, and inferred that these "two cultures" may, indeed, meet but rarely actually blend. In dialectic opposition, it may be proposed that *every* man, whether or not he professes scientific or humanistic pretensions, cherishes the *same* fundamental (Ur) values, to wit:

First, basic needs for health, skill and longevity so that he

---

*Allen Wheelis, in an article entitled "The Vocational Hazards of Psychoanalysis," points out that among the greatest of these is the defensive isolation of the analyst in his magical self-convictions: "A living science is more concerned with probing its unknowns than in praising its knowns, and he who cannot live with some fundamental uncertainties is not an investigator but a pilgrim."

may explore and control his material milieu. I have called this the first, or physical, Ur defense.

Second, deep desires for human friendships and alliances, to ameliorate his tragic loneliness and cement his communal welfare, the second, or social, Ur-adaptation.

Third, a search for the significance of his existence in relation to some cosmic or religious system, the final Ur-seeking for transcendence.*

Having thus sketched these triple themes, we can develop them contrapuntally by showing: a) that the "physical sciences" too have evolved from naive "materialism" toward an acceptance of these humanistic values, and b) that on the other hand the "humanities" by a more adroit use of Occam's razor (*v.s*), can shave their own polyglot and protean concepts down toward more simple and generalized formulae, on the model of the now familiar $E = mc^2$.

Let us, therefore, first attempt a brief, nonmathematical excursion into theoretical physics to indicate that even in this esoteric environment, we never actually leave the familiar field of human values, their therapeutic import, and perhaps their augury for the future of mankind.

Fugue and Variations: The Value of a Wave-Particle

Twenty-three centuries ago, Democritus, with classic confidence, wrote "Sweet and bitter, cold and warm as well as all the colors . . . exist but in opinion and not in reality; what really

---

*In all the recent psychoanalytic literature only S. Novey seems to have arrived, a bit later but probably independently, at quite similar formulations. These quotations from Novey are apropos: "I have postulated certain delusions which present, as it were, a necessary operation, based on what we describe as faith, which are essential if man is to function as a mature being . . . sharp delineation between the . . . neurotic and psychotic has been too rigid and . . . we have been prone to overlook or describe as dysfunction certain synthetic operations within the mature person which I perceive as constructive delusions. Man's capacity to delude himself . . . is essential to his very existence, however mature he may be. . . . Psychoanalysis cannot and must not do more than alter a malfunctioning personal myth so as to allow this myth to operate."

exists are unchangeable particles, atoms, and their motions in empty space." Galileo, too, postulated a solid physical substrate for the subjectivity of color, taste, smell, sound, touch and pain; so also, Locke, while admitting the evanescence of such "secondary sensations" nevertheless insisted on an external reality in which "shape, motion and solidity were primary qualities inherent in the object itself." The German mathematician Leibniz likewise maintained the eternity of his "monads" but recognized the quality of subjectivism thus: "I am able to prove that not only light, color, heat and the like, but motion, shape and extension, too, are merely *apparent* qualities." Then, despite the mysterious ubiquity of Planck's constant h, came the revolution of quantum physics, which, according to Barnett,

> . . . demolished two pillars of the old science, causality and determinism. For by dealing in terms of statistics and probabilities, it abandons all idea that nature exhibits an inexorable sequence of cause and effect . . . and the hope that science . . . can forecast the history of the universe.

Other former tangibles of sense and sequence likewise disappeared; again, to quote Barnett,

> A scientist can do no more than report his observations. And so if he performs two experiments with different instruments and one seems to reveal that light is made up of particles and the other that light is made up of waves, he must accept both results, regarding them not as contradictory but as complementary. By itself neither concept suffices to explain light, but together they do. Both are necessary to describe reality and it is meaningless to ask which is really true. For in the abstract lexicon of quantum physics, there is no such word as "really." . . . It is futile, moreover, to hope that the invention of more delicate tools may enable man to penetrate much farther into the microcosm. There is an indeterminacy about all the events of the atomic universe which refinements of measurement and observation can never dispel.

James Jeans admitted that theoretical physics led even further into affective solipsism by acknowledging that "it is probably as meaningless to discuss how much room an electron takes up as it is to discuss how much room a fear, an anxiety or an uncertainty takes up."

So vanishes "external reality." Yet precisely because man could not withstand the anxiety of a world in which objectivity and certainty were thus made ever asymptotic or nebulous, he continued to place a high value on the notion of *predictability*. Hence, even Heisenberg, despite his mathematically exquisite demonstrations of the ineffability of "ultimate substance" (as extended recently to all epistemology by Godel) was nevertheless intrigued by the circumstance that the arcane equations of quantum physics yield predictions far more probable (as witness the statistical near certainty of gross nuclear reactions) than could be derived from any model (e.g., a "wave-particle") that could be visualized by man. Einstein's aspirations for the Unified Field Theory were similar; wrote he,

> The ground aim of all science [is] to cover the greatest number of empirical facts by logical deductions from the smallest possible number of hypotheses or axioms.

Einstein, however, was always explicit as to the inescapable anthropocentricity of both "fact" and "value:" ". . . concepts are free creations of the human mind and are not, however it may seem, uniquely determined by the external world." Alfred North Whitehead, despite his disclaimer, put it more poetically: "Nature gets credit which in truth should be reserved for ourselves: the rose for its scent, the nightingale for his song, and the sun for its radiance. The poets are entirely mistaken. . . . Nature is a dull affair, soundless, scentless, colorless; merely the hurrying of material, endlessly, meaninglessly." Freud, too, discerningly commented in an early discussion of the Vienna Psychoanalytic Society, "Our understanding reaches as far as our anthropomorphism."

A curious byproduct of these psychological considerations was the revivification among physicists of the concept of free will. Again to quote Barnett,

> A wave electron, a proton, a wave of probability, cannot be visualized; they are simply symbols useful and expressing the mathematical

relationship of the microcosm. [But] if physical events are indeterminate and the future is unpredictable, then perhaps the unknown quantity called "mind" may yet guide man's destiny among the infinite uncertainties of a capricious universe.

The Ur-faith in Common Endeavor

With materialistic certainty thus negated, man understandably sought a second Ur-defense against his primal anxieties, namely alliance with his fellows for comfort and security, but, unfortunately, again with only equivocal success. It has been said in diverse ways that we live in an age when one must *call* his neighbor "friend" yet *act* as though he were a rival and perhaps an enemy; or, as noted, the anthropologists in their search for the missing link between anthropoid apes and civilized man, have discovered it in *us*. And yet man continues to long for human fellowship, both by historical loyalties to his predecessors and through improved communications and accords with his compatriots across space and culture. In the advance of knowledge, there is no better example of this than the communal endeavors of scientists themselves for the general enlightenment of mankind. In the "natural sciences" and philosophy, medieval scholars increasingly acknowledged their common debts to the classical Greeks; in physics, Newton later attributed his broadened perspectives to "standing on the shoulders of giants" and Einstein derived the inspiration for his General Theory of Relativity from the iconoclastic experiments of Michelson and Morley and from the Lorentz Transformations. In ecology and economics, Malthus, Marx, Engels, Lenin, *et al.,* extrapolating Plato, Hobbes and Machiavelli, proposed that merely by regulating man's power struggles, they could indeed achieve earthly Utopias. Immanuel Kant preserved the values of individual will and freedom but added the *categorical imperative of social commitment* by insisting that each human must act in such ways that could be "generalized as norms for all mankind." Bronowski added the scientist's touch:

> Sentences constructed with *is* usually have a verifiable meaning, but sentences constructed with *ought* never have . . . [But if man]

accepts no evidence and no judgement except his own, he has no tools with which to frame an answer.

Bentley Glass comes even closer to the basic humanistic sources and values of all science:

> By examining critically the nature, origins and methods of science we logically arrive at a conclusion that science is ineluctably involved in questions of values, is inescapably committed to standards of right and wrong and unavoidably moves . . . toward social aims. . . . Man's own values grew out of his evolutionary origins and his struggle against a hostile environment for survival. Our highest ethical values—the love of the mother for her child and the man for his mate, and the willingness to sacrifice one's own life for the safety of the family or tribe, and the impulse to care for the weak, the suffering, the helpless—all of these, too, had the same primitive beginnings . . . [The] primary function of science is not simply that of appeasing the individual scientist's curiosity about his environment—on the contrary, it is that of adjusting man to man. . . . Somehow, there has crept into our writings . . .that science is "objective" while the humanistic studies are "subjective." What a profound mistake! . . . The scientist is a man, through his science doing good and evil to other men, and [deservedly] receiving from them blame and praise."

In medicine, we have the aspiring *montagnards,* miracle-workers and martyrs for whose cooperative and cumulative work humanity can be eternally grateful; indeed, physicians and psychiatrists, being both scientists and humanitarians, can thus especially well understand how inextricably fused are the respective values in both fields.

The Ur-faith of Existential Meaning

However, mundane knowledge and mortal alliances—the first two Ur-defenses—could not adequately resolve the agonizing anxieties of individual existence and cosmic significance; ergo, men of all "cultures" have always resorted either to various forms of narcissistic self-sufficiency, or to their projections into transcendent systems variously labeled philosophies, cosmologies or religions. As to the first or introspective mode of this third

Ur-defense, nearly two dozen centuries before Husserl or Camus, Plato wrote,

> The true lover of knowledge is always striving after *Being* . . . he will not rest at those multitudinous phenomena whose existence is appearance only.

Projecting homocentrism to the astronomic sphere, Kepler and Copernicus believed that the very stars were intimately concerned with mortal man, and that therefore his dealings with his fellows were astrologically written and predictable. But since the stars themselves were presumably but the puppets of God, Bishop Berkeley thus brought man into contact with Divinity:

> All the choir of heaven and furniture of earth, in a word, all those bodies which compose the mighty frame of the world, have not any substance without the mind. . . . So long as they are not actually perceived by me, or do not exist in my mind, or that of any other created spirit, they must either have no existence at all, or else subsist in the mind of some Eternal Spirit.

In an even more frankly anthropomorphic vein, Eddington conceived of God in the image of Eddington as a "master mathematician," whereas, in a poignant extension of dyadic devotion, the encyclopedist Auguste Comte, who had founded the formal science of sociology, spent the last years of his life as the high priest of a religion which worshipped his dead wife Clothilde as the Queen of Heaven. But perhaps it was Einstein, superb scientist, humble humanist and profound philosopher, who put man's third Ur-faith most eloquently:

> I cannot believe that God plays dice with the world. . . . The most beautiful and most profound emotion we can experience is the sensation of the mystical. It is the sower of all true science. He to whom this emotion is a stranger, who can no longer wonder and stand rapt in awe, is as good as dead. To know that what is impenetrable to us really exists, manifesting itself as the highest wisdom and the most radiant beauty which our dull faculties can comprehend only in their most primitive forms—this knowledge, this feeling is at the center of true religiousness.

Semantic Reflections: Andante Sostenuto

But there is yet another heuristic source of insight into man's seekings which we psychiatrists often vitiate by parochial or constricted interpretations: the living history and dialectic wealth immanent in our languages and our legends. As examples of the latter, Narcissus, despite our misuse of the word "narcissism," did not "love *himself*;" more subtly, he forswore his friend Almeinas and his mistress Echo to become entranced with his self-interpreted *image* (i.e., the first Ur-solipsism). So also, the infant Oedipus survived physical hardships (again Ur-need I) through a shepherd's kindness (Ur-alliance II), sought his social "identity" as a youth (once more II) and, though he suffered tragedy and exile, dared to enter the Grove of Colonus, master of the Fates themselves and enter Olympus as a demigod (Ur-faith and triumph III). H. J. Home explores the role of such quasi-religious myths in "classical" analytic exegeses thus:

> Kleinian comment (on Freudian doctrine) questioned the phallic interpretation of clinical material which it felt patently referred to the breast. No one has suggested a method of deciding such an issue and so it presumably remains an open question like the pronunciation of tomato. . . . In the event of disagreement in discussion the appeal was almost invariably to the literature and not to the fact. . . . Similar recourse to the literature seems to occur only in religious writing and in our own day in Communist theory. . . . At times psychoanalytic theory appears all too like a house which a bereaved spouse, in piety, preserves just as it was on the day of the great loss. . . . Reification is deification!

But perhaps the most concentrated insights are retained in the very root words of medicine and psychiatry: *health, sanity* and *therapy. Mens sanis in corpora sano* expressed for our classic forebears the indissoluble values of bodily well-being, social usefulness and "mental" serenity and creativity, whereas our term *therapy* is derived from the Greek *therapeien,* meaning simply and significantly, *human service.* But even more richly significant is the word *health,* traceable to Anglo-Saxon *hal* or *hol.* From these roots are derived not only physical *haleness* and medical *healing,* but also the congenial greeting *hail!* (hail-ho, hello, heil) *friend,* and the value concepts of philosophic *wholesomeness* and religious *holiness.* It may be that our term *illness* is also related to evil-ness, from Anglo-Saxon *yfel,* evil. Ergo, once again Greek, Roman and Gaul have transmitted to us, through syncretic terms in which our tripartite wishes and values merge, man's ancient wisdom of the essential—and thereby cherished and valued—physical, social and therapeutic aspects of health and sanity.

Finale Therapeutique

Our preceding discourse may thus help us to clarify and integrate the following tripartite addition to the rationale of human treatment, as extended beyond that applicable to animal neuroses.

First, as to its *Physical Aspects*: Regardless of whether the patient's (L. *patiens,* sufferer) complaints are considered as primarily "organic" or "psychosomatic," we must ameliorate bodily discomfort and dysfunction by every medical and surgical means available including, when indicated, carefully prescribed sedatives or ataractics temporarily useful to dull painful memories, diminish apprehension and quiet agitation. However, in nearly all medical and surgical specialties we recognize that after such initial rest and relief, we must also reevoke the patient's initiative and recultivate his talents and skills (Ur-power I) so that he can regain the competence and confidence that can come only from useful accomplishment.

Second, as to his *Social Commitments*: Since no man is an "Islande unto Himself," the wise physician must also recognize that his patient may be deeply concerned about *interpersonal* familial, sexual, financial, career and related problems that may also seriously affect his physical as well as his social well-being. This involves an exploration, varying in depth and duration but always discerning and tactful, of the patient's psychologic assets

and vulnerabilities, the attitudes, goals and incentives stemming
from his past experiences, the wide variations of "values" and
their derived "moral judgments among various cultures—"moral"
being derived from L. *mores,* meaning simply local custom—
the channeling effects of past successes or the disruptive residues
they left on patterns of effective (normal), socially ineffective
(neurotic) or bizarrely unrealistic (psychotic) conduct, the ways
in which these patterns relieve or exacerbate his current diffi-
culties, and which of them are most accessible to various methods
of medicopsychiatric therapy exquisitely oriented to the patient's
aspirations in his social milieu. It has been my gratifying experience that with this orientation, many intelligent, sensitive non-
psychiatrists possessed of a sympathetic, dynamic *einfuhlung* can,
in time they can readily make available, conduct the essential
psychotherapy required. In brief, this will consist of using gentle
reasoning, personal example and progressive reorientative experiences to help the patient correct his prejudices and past
misconceptions, abandon infantile or childlike patterns of trans-
action that have long since lost their effectiveness, revise his objectives and values, and thereby adopt a more realistic, productive and lastingly rewarding ("mature") style of life. In this
skillfully guided reeducation (good psychotherapy is about as
"nondirective" as good surgery), the enlightened cooperation of
his family, friends, employer and others may, with the patient's
consent, be utilized to the full. By such means the patient's Ur-
alliances will be strengthened by renewed communal solidarity
and security—a *sine qua non* of comprehensive treatment.

METAPHYSICAL. Lastly, in pursuit of the third or cosmic Ur-
value, the patient's religious, philosophic or other convictions,
instead of being deprecated or undermined, should be respected
and strengthened insofar as they furnish him with what each
of us requires: a belief in life's meaning and purpose. In this
deepest sense, medicine, being a humanitarian science, can never
be in conflict with philosophy or religion, since all three seem

to be designed by a beneficent providence to preserve, cheer and comfort man, and thereby constitute a trinity to be respected by those of us deeply concerned with our triple roles as physicians, social guides and philosophic mentors to those who seek our help in all of these spheres.

History Teaches that History Cannot Teach Us, And Yet . . .

With so many consistencies between past and present, can we also extrapolate the design of the future? Let us again group tentative predictions about man's behavior around our now familiar Ur-trilogy.

UR-PRESERVATION IN THE FUTURE. Despite the perennial legends of Pandora, Golem, Frankenstein, *et al.* in almost every mythology, and the knowledge that we now have at hand enough nuclear explosives to kill every human on earth ten times over, I doubt—I *must* doubt—that our race is really hell-bent on suicide. Rather, we shall discover dimensions and forces yet unconceived; we shall distill the ocean and dessicate its fish for tasteless food; we shall conquer cancer and induce new diseases; we shall explore the moon and find it a dust heap; in short, we shall continue to match our puny technologies against a universe ever beyond man's finite ken or control—and probably be more bewildered by the endless cosmos than ever.

UR-SOCIETY IN THE FUTURE. A world community is the only alternative to Armageddon, and since *Homo sapiens* is a single, universally fecund species, differences of "race" or "color" will eventually become about as distinguishable as Lombard, Hittite or Etruscan strains are now in their mixed descendants. Men will become more alike—and perhaps a little friendlier.

UR-THEOLOGY OF THE FUTURE. Finally, we shall develop a deeper sense of cosmic existence that will transcend the symbolic legends, rituals and theocracies of our current religions further than they have progressed from the animistic worship of our savage ancestors. And when man achieves this breadth of vision and depth of understanding, he may also become humbler, kinder, wiser—and perhaps a bit happier.

Meta-clinical Summary

A review of the evolving epistemology of science indicates that even in a discipline as "exact" as physics, "objectivity" is unattainable and operational formulae become merely subjective evaluations of statistical vectors. In this sense, if an heuristic and semantic analysis were done of the essentials of what men in all times, places and cultures have deemed deserving of effort and courage, the following ultimate (Ur) values would emerge.

First, the pursuit of physical health, skill and longevity with which to explore and control the material universe.

Second, the seeking for human friendships and alliances to ameliorate loneliness and cement communal welfare.

Third, the aspiration toward a transcendent faith that would lend significance to man's otherwise meaningless existence.

In the cumulative wisdom of our language, the term *health* (from Anglo-Saxon *hal* or *hōl*) has three parallel derivations: physical *haleness,* the friendly salutation *hail!* and finally *wholesome* and *holy.* Thus, also indicated are the basic objectives of all medical and psychiatric therapy:

First, to restore our patients' physical well-being skills, and creative potentials; concurrently, to welcome and guide them to resume warm and fruitful human companionships; and simultaneously, to help them regain basic serenities within themselves, with their fellow men and with their individually adaptive social, philosophic and theologic faiths.

As mere mortals, we can do no more.

REFERENCES

1. AARONS, L.; SCHULMAN, J.; MASSERMAN, J. H., and ZIMMAR, C. P.: Behavioral adaptations after parietal cortex ablation in the neonate macaque. In J. Wortis (Ed.), *Recent Advances in Biological Psychiatry,* vol. 4, 1962, p. 347.

2. ALLEE, W. C.: *Cooperation among Animals.* New York, Henry Schuman, 1951.

3. ANDREW, J. J.: Evolution of facial expression. *Science, 142*:1034, 1963.

4. ARBIT, J.; YACORZYNSKI, G., *et al.*: Personal communication, 1965.

5. ASHBY, W. R.: *Design for a Brain.* New York, Wiley, 1952.

6. BAILEY, P.: Modern attitudes toward the relationship of the brain in behavior. *Arch Gen Psychiat (Chicago), 2*:361, 1960.

7. BAILEY, P.: Cortex and mind. In J. Scher (Ed.), *Theories of Mind.* New York, Free Press, 1962.

8. BAILEY, P.: The great psychiatric revolution. *Amer J Psychiat, 113*: 387-405, 1956.

9. BAILEY, P.: *Sigmund the Unserene.* Springfield, Thomas, 1965.

10. BAMBRIDGE, R.: Early experience and sexual behavior in the domestic chicken. *Science, 136*:259, 1962.

11. BARNETT, LINCOLN: *The Universe and Dr. Einstein.* New York, Mentor, 1954.

12. BEACH, F. A.: The snark was a boojum. *Amer Psychol, 5*:115, 1950.

13. BELLAK, L.: An experimental exploration of the psychoanalytic process. *Psychoanal Quart, 25*:385-414, 1956.

14. BENDICH, A.: Studies on the biological activity of the desoxyribunucleid acids. *Dis Nerv Syst, 22*:9, 1961.

15. BERCEL, N. A.: The influence of schizophrenic serum on the behavior of the spider. *Arch Gen Psychiat (Chicago), 2*:189, 1960.

16. BERTALANFFY, L. VON.: An essay on the relativity of categories. *Phil Sci, 22*:24, 1955.

17. BEST, C. H., and TAYLOR, N. B.: *The Physiologic Basis of Medical Practice.* 6th ed, Baltimore, Williams & Wilkins, 1959, p. 895.

18. BEST, J. B.: Protopsychology. *Sci Amer, 208*:55, 1963.

19. BHARUCHA-REID, R. P.: Latent learning in earthworms. *Science, 123*:222, 1956.

20. BIEBER, I.: A critique of the libido theory. *Amer J Psychoanal, 81*:52, 1958.

21. BINGHAM, H. C.: Sex development in apes. *Comp Physiol Monogr,* 5, 1928.
22. BLOOM, J. B.; DAVIS, N., and WECHT, D. H.: Effect on the liver of long-term tranquilizing medication. *Amer J Psychiat, 121*:788-797, 1965.
23. BONNER, J. T.: *Cells and Societies.* Princeton, Princeton, 1955.
24. BOWLBY, J.: The nature of the child's tie to his mother. *Int J Psychoanal, 39*:350, 1959.
25. BOYCOTT, B. B.: Learning in the octopus. *Sci Amer, 212*:42-50, 1965.
26. BRADY, J. V.: The experimental analysis of emotional behavior. *Proc XIV Int Cong Psychol.* Amsterdam, Heath Hallard, 1955. pp. 148-50.
27. BRADY, J. V.: Ulcers in "executive" monkeys. *Sci Amer, 199*:95, 1959.
28. BRADY, J. V.; PORTER, R. W.; CONRAD, D. G., and MASON, J. W.: Avoidance behavior and the development of gastroduodenal ulcers. *J Exp Anal Behav, 1*:69, 1958.
29. BRANDT, L.: Operation Diana. *Child-Family Dig, 15*:19, 1956.
30. BRIDGES, K. M.: Human imprinting. *Child Dev, 3*:324, 1932.
31. BRONOWSKI, J.: The sense of human dignity. In *Science and Human Values.* New York, Messner, 1956.
32. BROWN, F. A.: The rhythmic nature of animals and plants. *Sci Amer, 47*:147, 1959.
33. BRUNSWICK, E.: *Perception and the Representative Design of Psychological Experiments.* Berkeley, U. of Calif., 1956.
34. BURSTON, R., and DELGADO, J.M.R.: Positive reinforcement induced by intracerebral stimulation in the monkey. *J Comp Physiol Psychol, 51*:6, 1958.
35. BURTON, M.: *Animal Courtship.* New York, Praeger, 1954.
36. BURTON, F.: *Personal Narrative of a Pilgrimage to El-Medina and Mecca.* London, Bell, 2 vols., 1898.
37. BUTLER, R. A.: Curiosity in monkeys. *Sci Amer, 190*:70, 1954.
38. BYKOV, K. M.: Cerebral cortex and the inner organs. *Arch Biol, 3*:54, 1939.
39. CALHOUN, J. B.: Population density and social pathology. *Sci Amer, 206*:139, 1962.
40. CANNON, W. B.: *The Way of the Investigator.* New York, Norton, 1945.
41. CASPARI, E. W., and MARSHAK, R. E.: The rise and fall of Lysenko. *Science, 149*:257-278, 1965.
42. CHAPMAN, L.; HENKLE, L. E., and WOLFF, H. G.: Organic effects of stress. *Amer J Psychiat, 117*:193, 1960.

43. CHEN, S. C.: Interaction in ants. *Physiol Zool, 10*:420, 1937.

44. CHRISTIAN, J. J.: Adrenocortical and gonadal responses of female mice to increased population density. *Proc Soc Exp Biol Med, 104*:330-332, 1960.

45. CLARK, L. D.: A comparative view of aggressive behavior. *Proc Amer Psychopath Ass,* Western Division, Salt Lake City, Sept., 1961; also in *Med Trib, 5*:18, 1964.

46. CLEGHORN, R. H., and GRAHAM, B. F.: Studies of adrenal cortical activity in psycho-neurotic subjects. *Amer J Psychiat, 106*:658, 1950.

47. COBB, S.: Instincts. *Amer J Psychiat, 112*:149, 1955.

48. COLBY, K. M.: *Energy and Structure in Psychoanalysis.* New York, Ronald, 1955.

49. COMMONER, B.: In defense of biology. *Science, 133*:1745, 1961.

50. CONGER, J. V.: The effects of alcohol on conflict behavior. *Quart J Stud Alcohol, 12*:1-29, 1951.

51. CONRADI, E.: Song and call-notes of English sparrows when reared by canaries. *Amer J Psychol, 16*:190, 1905.

52. COPE, C. L.: Some adrenal facts and fancies. *Proc Roy Soc Med, 58*:55, 1965.

53. CRAIG, W.: The crossbreeding of pigeons. *Amer J Sociol, 14*:86, 1908.

54. CRAIG, W.: Male doves reared in isolation. *J Anim Behav, 4*:121, 1914.

55. CROSS, H. A., and HARLOW, H. F.: Prolonged and progressive effects of partial isolation on macaque monkeys. *J Exp Res Pers, 1*:39-49, 1965.

56. DARLINGTON, D. C.: The origin of Darwinism. *Sci Amer, 50*:200, 1959.

57. DELGADO, J.M.R.: Cerebral structures involved in transmission and elaboration of noxious stimulation. *J Neurophysiol, 18*:261, 1955.

58. DELGADO, J.M.R.: Electronic command of movement and behavior. *Trans NY Acad Sci, 21*:689, 1959.

59. DELGADO, J.M.R.: Emotional behavior in animals and humans. *Psychol Res Rep, 12*:259, 1960.

60. DELGADO, J.M.R.; ROSVOLD, H.E., and LOONEY, E.: Evoking conditioned fear by electrical stimulation of subcortical structures in the monkey brain. *J Comp Physiol Psychol, 49*:373, 1956.

61. DEMENT, W. C.: Experimental dream studies. In Masserman, J. H. (Ed.), *Science and Psychoanalysis,* New York, Grune, Vol. 7, 1964, pp. 129-160.

62. DENENBERG, V. H.; HUDGENS, G. A., and ZARROW, M. X.: Mice reared with rats. *Science, 143*:380-381.

63. DENENBERG, V.H., and MORTON, J. R. C.: Effects of weaning on problem-solving behavior. *J Comp Physiol Psychol, 55*:1096-1098, 1962.

64. DENENBERG, V. H.; OTTINGER, D. R., and STEPHENS, M. W.: Maternal factors in growth and behavior of the rat. *Child Dev, 33*: 65-71, 1962.

65. DEUTSCH, J. S., and HOWARTEN, C. I.: Evocation by fear of a habit learned for electrical stimulation of the brain. *Science, 136*:1057, 1962.

66. DOBIE, J. R.: The roadrunner in fact and folklore. *Arizona Highways, 34*, 1948.

67. DUCASSE, C. J.: *A Philosophical Scrutiny of Religion.* New York, Ronald, 1952.

68. EDWARDES, A., and MASTERS, R. F. L.: *The Cradle of Erotica.* New York, Julian, 1952.

69. EINSTEIN, A.: *Philosopher, Scientist.* Evanston, Library of Living Philosophers, 1949.

70. EYSENCK, H. J.: The effects of psychotherapy. *Int J Psychiat, 1*: 97-143, 1965.

71. FERSTER, C. B.: Arithmetic behavior in chimpanzees. *Sci Amer, 210*:98-106, 1964.

72. FISCHBERG, M., and BLACKLER, A. W.: How cells specialize. *Sci Amer, 205*:124, 1961.

73. FISHER, A. E.: Chemical stimulation of the brain. *Sci Amer, 210*:60, 1964.

74. FOREL, A.: *The Social World of the Ants Compared to That of Man.* New York, Boni, 1929.

75. FREED, E. X.: The effect of alcohol upon approach behavior in the rat. *Newsletter Res Psychol, 8* (No. 1): 18-19.

76. FREED, E. X.: The effect of alcohol upon approach-avoidance conflict. *Quart J Stud Alcohol.* In press.

77. FRENCH, J. W.: Individual differences in paramecium. *J Comp Psychol, 30*:451, 1940.

78. FRENCH, T.: Interrelations between psychoanalysis and Pavlov. *Amer J Psychiat, 89*:1165, 1933.

79. FREUD, S.: Postscript to a discussion on lay analysis. *Coll Papers,* 1937.

80. FREUD, S.: Goal, mechanism and integrative field. *Psychosom Med, 3*:226, 1941.

81. FREUD, S.: *Leonardo da Vinci.* New York, Random, 1947.

82. FREUD, S.: *An Outline of Psychoanalysis.* New York, Norton, 1949.

83. FREUD, S.: *The Question of Lay Analysis.* New York, Norton, 1950.

84. FREUD, S.: *An Autobiographical Study.* London, Hogarth, 1950.
85. FREUD, S.: *The Origins of Psychoanalysis: Letters to Wilhelm Fleiss, 1887-1902.* New York, Basic Books, 1954.
86. FRINGS, H., and JUMBER, J.: Preliminary studies on the use of a specific sound to repel starlings. *Science, 119:*318, 1954.
87. FULLER, J. L,: *Nature and Nurture: A Modern Synthesis.* New York, Doubleday, 1954.
88. GANTT, W. H.: *The Origin and Development of Behavior Disorders in Dogs.* New York, Psychosom Monographs, 1942.
89. GERARD, R. W.: Units and concepts of biology. *Science, 125:*429, 1957.
90. GLASS, B.: The ethical basis of science. *Science, 150:*1254-67, 1965.
91. GIBBONS, J. L.: Cortisol secretion rate in depressive illness. *Arch Gen Psychiat (Chicago), 10:*572, 1964.
92. GILLARD, E. T.: The evolution of bowerherds. *Sci Amer, 209:*30, 1963.
93. GINSBERG, B. E.: Genetics as a tool in the study of behavior. In *Perspectives in Biology.* In press.
94. GLASS, B.: Discussion of the genetics symposium. *Amer J Psychiat, 113:*504, 1956.
95. GOODALL, J.: Chimpanzees. *Nat Geographic, 124:*293, 1963.
96. GOODALL, J.: Chimpanzee tool-users. *Science, 146:*801, 1964.
97. GREEN, J. D.: The hippocampus. *Physiol Rev, 44:*561, 1964.
98. GREENWAY, J.: One man's meat is another man's person. *Fact, 1:*18, 1964.
99. GRINKER, R. R., SR.: Anxiety as a significant variable. *Arch Gen Psychiat (Chicago), 1:*537, 1959.
100. GRINKER, R. R., and SPIEGEL, J. P.: *Men under Stress.* Philadelphia, Blakeston, 1945.
101. GUHL, M.: The social order of chickens. *Sci Amer, 194:*43, 1966.
102. HAFORD, C. B.: Rank of mothers and sons in bands of rhesus monkeys. *Sci Amer, 141:*356, 1963.
103. HALSTEAD, W. C.: *Brain and Intelligence.* Chicago, U. of Chicago, 1947.
104. HAM, C. C.: Genes and the psyche. *Amer J Psychiat, 119:*828, 1963.
105. HARLOW, H. F.: The development of learning in the rhesus monkey. *Sci Amer, 47:*459, 1959.
106. HARLOW, H. F.: Love in the infant monkey. *Sci Amer, 200:*68, 1959.
107. HARRISON, B.: *Orangutan.* Garden City, Doubleday, 1963.
108. HEATH, R. G., et al.: *Studies in Schizophrenia: a Multidisciplinary Approach to Mind-Brain Relationships.* Cambridge, Harvard, 1954.

109. HEATH, R. G.; MONROE, R. B., and MICKLE, W. A.: Stimulation of the amygdaloid nucleus in a schizophrenia patient. *Amer J Psychiat, 111*:862, 1955.

110. HEATH, R. G., *et al.*: Reappraisal of biological aspects of psychiatry. *J Neuropsychiat, 2*:111, 1961.

111. HEBB, D. O.: *A Textbook of Psychology.* Philadelphia, Saunders, 1958.

112. HEINFORTH, O.: Beitrage sur Biologie. *Int Ornith Kongs, 5*:25, 1910.

113. HELLWOLD, H.: Untersuchungen uber trie starken bei tieren. *Z Psychol, 123*:38, 1931.

114. HESS, E.: "Imprinting" in animals. *Sci Amer, 198*:81, 1958.

115. HESS, E.: Imprinting. *Science, 130*:133, 1959.

116. HIGGINS, J. W.; MAHL, G. F.; DELGADO, J.M.R., and HAMLIN, H.: Behavior changes during intercerebral electrical stimulation. *Arch Neurol Psychiat, 76*:319-419, 1956.

117. HILL, A. V.: Why biologics? *Report, 26,* 1957.

118. HIMWICH, H. E.: Emotional aspects of mind. In J. Scher (Ed.), *Theories of the Mind.* New York, Free Press, 1962.

119. HOEBEL, E. A.: *The Law of Primitive Man.* Cambridge, Harvard, 1954.

120. HOME, H. J.: The concept of mind. *Int J Psychoanal, 47*:42, 1966.

121. HORSFALL, F. V.: Heritance of acquired characteristics. *Science, 136*:4, 1962.

122. HORWITT, M. R.: Fact and artifact in the biology of schizophrenia. *Science, 124*:429, 1956.

123. HSU, F. L. K.: *Psychological Anthropology.* Homewood, Dorsey, 1961.

124. HUNTINGTON, E.: *Season of Birth.* New York, Wiley, 1938.

125. HUXLEY, T. H.: *Man's Place in Nature.* London, Thomas, Ltd., 1898.

126. INGALLS, T. H.: Etiology of mongolism. *Amer J Dis Child, 74*:147, 1947.

127. JACOBSEN, E., and SKAARUP, Y.: Experimental induction of conflict-behavior in cats: its use in pharmacological investigations. *Acta Pharmacol (Kobenhavn), 11*:117, 1955.

128. JENNINGS, H. S.: *The Biologic Basis of Human Nature.* New York, Norton, 1930.

129. JENSEN, D. D.: Learning. *Science, 126*:1341, 1957.

130. JOHN, E. R.: The psychophysiology of mind. In J. Scher (Ed.), *Theories of the Mind.* New York, Free Press, 1962.

131. KALLMAN, E. J.: Heredity and eugenics. *Amer J Psychiat, 115*:503, 1959.

132. KALOGERAKIS, M. G.: The role of olfaction in sexual development. *Psychosom Med, 25*:42, 1963.

133. KANNER, L.: *Child Psychiatry.* 3rd ed., Springfield, Thomas, 1957.

134. KATZ, D.: *Animals and Man.* New York, Longmans Green, 1937.

135. KAVANAU, J. L.: Confinement, adaptation and compulsory regimes in laboratory studies. *Science, 143*:490, 1963.

136. KEELEY, K.: Prenatal influence on behavior of offspring of crowded mice. *Science, 135*:43, 1962.

137. KEMPF, E. J.: The social and sexual behavior of the infra-human primates and some comparable facts in human behavior. *Psychoanal Rev, 4*:127, 1917.

138. KETY, S. S.: Biochemical theories of schizophrenia. *Science, 129*: 1528, 1590, 1959.

139. KETY, S. S.: A biologist examines mind and behavior. *Science, 132*:1861, 1960.

140. KING, J. A.: Parameters relevant to determining the affect of early experiences upon the adult behavior of animals. *Psychol Bull, 5*:46, 1958.

141. KLOPFER, P. H.: Is imprinting a chesire cat? *Behav Sci, 12*:122, 1967.

142. KLOPFER, P. H.: The social behavior of prairie dogs. *Sci Amer, 201,* 1959.

143. KLUVER, A., and BUCY, P. C.: Functions of the temporal lobe in monkeys. *Arch Neurol Psychiat, 42*:979-1000, 1939.

144. KOHLER, W.: *The Mentality of Apes.* New York, Harcourt, 1929.

145. KORTLAND, A.: Chimpanzees in the wild. *Sci Amer, 206*:128, 1962.

146. KREBS, C. J.: Lemming migration. *Arctic Inst N Amer,* 1965.

147. KUO, Z. Y.: Genesis of the cat's responses toward the rat. *J Comp Psychol, 11*:1, 1930.

148. KURLAND, H. D.: Steroid excretion in depressive disorders. *Arch. Gen Psychiat (Chicago), 10*:554, 1964b.

149. LANGER, S.: *Philosophy in a New Key.* New York, Mentor, 1942.

150. LAPEN, I., and GROONER, M. E.: JR.: The baboon colony of the Southwest Foundation. *JAMA, 186*:3, 1963.

151. LAPOUSE, R., and MONK, M.: *Med News,* August, 1958.

152. LASHLEY, K. S.: Dynamic processes in perception. In Delafresnaze, J. F. (Ed.), *Brain Mechanisms and Consciousness.* Springfield, Thomas, 1954.

153. LEBLOND, C. P.: Extra-hormonal factors in maternal behavior. *Proc Soc Exp Biol Med, 38*:66, 1938.

154. LEE, B. S.: Delayed auditory feedback. *J Acoust Soc Amer, 22*:824, 1950.

155. LeGros Clark, W. E.: *The Antecedents of Man*. Chicago, Quadrangle, 1960.
156. Lehrman, D. S.: The reproductive behavior of ring doves. *Sci Amer, 211*:48, 1964.
157. LeMagnen, J. H.: L'olfaction. *J Physiol, 45*:285, 1953.
158. Levik, G. M.: Antarctic penguins. London, Trench Trubner, 1914.
159. Levy, D.: The relation of animal psychology to psychiatry. In I. Galdston (Ed.), *Medicine and Science*. New York, Int Univ, 1954.
160. Levy, O. M.: Experiments in the sucking reflex and social behavior of dogs. *Amer J Orthopsychiat, 4*:203, 1934.
161. Liddell, H. S.: Discussion of Konrad Lorenz. *Proc Ctr Postgrad Trans*, New York, October 23, 1958.
162. Lilly, J. C.: Some considerations regarding basic mechanisms of positive and negative motivation. *Amer J Psychiat, 115*:113, 1956.
163. Lilly, J. C.: The psychophysiologic bases for two kinds of instincts. *J Amer Psychoanal Ass, 8*:659, 1960.
164. Lilly, J. C.: Distress call of the bottlenose dolphin and evoked behavior responses. *Science, 139*:116, 1963.
165. Limbaugh, C.: Cleaning symbioses. *Sci Amer, 206*:78, 1961.
166. Lindauer, M.: House hunt. *Sci Amer, 196*:70, 1958.
167. Linden, M. E.: Relationship between social attitudes toward aging and the delinquencies of youth. *Amer J Psychiat, 114*:444, 1957.
168. Loeb, J.: *The Organism as a Whole*. New York, Putnam, 1916.
169. Lorenz, K.: *King Solomon's Ring*. New York, Crowell, 1952.
170. Loveridge, A.: Notes on East African mammals. *J E Afr N H Soc, 16*:1938; *17*:1939.
171. Lowie, R.: *Primitive Society*. New York, Leneught, 1947.
172. McIlwain, P. D.: *Biochemistry of the Central Nervous System*. Boston, Little, 1955.
173. McLean, P. D.: The limbic system ("visceral brain") in relation to central gray and reticulum of the brain stem. *Psychosom Med, 17*:355, 1955.
174. McLean, P. D.: Psychosexual evaluation in monkeys. *J Nerv Ment Dis, 135*:209, 1962.
175. Magoun, H. W.: An ascending reticular activation system in the brain stem. *Arch Neurol Psychiat, 67*:155, 1952.
176. Malamud, N.: Psychiatric symptoms and the limbic lobe. *Bull Los Angeles Neurol Soc, 22*:131-139, 1957.
177. Malinowski, B.: *Sex and Repression in Savage Society*. New York, Harcourt, 1927.
178. Mandell, A. J.: Some determinants of indole excretion in man. *Recent Advances Biol Psychiat, 5*:237, 1963.

179. MANDELL, A. J.; SABOTT, I. M.; MANDELL, M. P., and KOLLAR, E. J.: The stress responsive indole substance in sleep deprivation. *Arch Gen Psychiat (Chicago), 10*:299-305, 1964.

180. MARMOR, J.: The role of instinct in human behavior. *Psychiatry, 5*: 509-516, 1942.

181. MARSHALL, A. J.: Bower birds. *Sci Amer, 194*:48, 1956.

182. MASLOW, A. H.: Role of dominance in the social and sexual behavior of infra-human primates. *J Genet Psychol, 48*:261, 1936.

183. MASSERMAN, J. H.: Psychobiologic dynamisms in behavior. *Psychiatry, 5*:341, 1942.

184. MASSERMAN, J. H.: Principles of biodynamics. *Trans NY Acad Sci, 61,* 1944.

185. MASSERMAN, J. H.: Report of the committee on animal experimentations, 1943-44. *Psychosom Med, 7*:46, 1945.

186. MASSERMAN, J. H.: Experimental neuroses and psychotherapy. *Arch Neurol Psychiat, 49*:43, 1943.

187. MASSERMAN, J. H.: Problems of the neuroses: an experimental approach. *Cincinnati J Med, 27*:73, 1946.

188. MASSERMAN, J. H.: A biodynamic psychoanalytic approach to the problems of feeling and emotion. In M. L. Reymert (Ed.), *Feelings and Emotions.* New York, McGraw, 1950.

189. MASSERMAN, J. H.: New experimental neuroses. *Sci Amer, 182*:38, 1950.

190. MASSERMAN, J. H.: Some current concepts of sexual behavior. *Psychiatry, 14*:67, 1951

191. MASSERMAN, J. H.: Psychoanalysis and biodynamics—an integration. *Int J Psa., 34*:34, 1953.

192. MASSERMAN, J. H.: *Principles of Dynamic Psychiatry.* 2nd ed., Philadelphia, Saunders, 1965.

193. MASSERMAN, J. H.: *Practice of Dynamic Psychiatry.* Philadelphia, Saunders, 1955.

194. MASSERMAN, J. H.: Experimental psychopharmacology and behavioral relativity. In P. Hoch and J. Zubin (Eds.), *Problems of Addiction and Habituation.* New York, Grune, 1958.

195. MASSERMAN, J. H.: Norms, neurotics and nepenthics. In J. M. Masserman (Ed.), *Biological Psychiatry.* New York, Grune, vol. I, 1959.

196. MASSERMAN, J. H.: Ethology, comparative biodynamics and psychoanalytic research. In J. H. Masserman, (Ed.), *Science and Psychoanalysis.* New York, Grune, vol. III, 1960, p. 20.

197. MASSERMAN, J. H.: Purview and comment. In T. T. Tourlentes (Ed.), *Research Approaches to Psychiatric Problems.* New York, Grune, 1962, p. 230.

198. MASSERMAN, J. H.: Drugs, brain and behavior. *J Neuropsychiat,* 3:5104, 1962.

199. MASSERMAN, J. H.: *Behavior and Neurosis.* (Classics Reprint), New York, Hafner, 1964.

200. MASSERMAN, J. H.: Anxiety: protean source of communication. In J. H. Masserman (Ed.), *Science and Psychoanalysis,* New York, Grune, vol. VIII, 1965, p. 1.

201. MASSERMAN, J. H.: Or shall we all commit suicide? In Masserman, J. H. (Ed.), *Current Psychiatric Therapies,* New York, Grune vol. II, 1962, p. 273.

202. MASSERMAN, J. H.: Man's eternal anxieties. *Illinois Med J, 127:* 375-561, 1966.

203. MASSERMAN, J. H. (Ed.): *Science and Psychoanalysis.* New York, Grune, vol. XII, 1967.

204. MASSERMAN, J. H.: *Modern Therapy of Behavior Disorders.* Dubuque, Brown, 1966.

205. MASSERMAN, J. H.: Ethology. In J. H. Masserman (Ed.), *Science and Psychoanalysis,* New York, Grune, vol. XII, 1967.

206. MASSERMAN, J. H.: Motion picture films on Experimental Neuroses; Alcohol; Masochism; Morphine, and Development of Behavior. Catalogue, Psychological Cinema Register, State University of Pa., Pa. 1938-1965.

207. MASSERMAN, J. H., and JACQUES, M. G.: Effects of cerebral electroshock on experimental neuroses in cats. *Amer J Psychiat, 104:*92, 1947.

208. MASSERMAN, J. H., and JACQUES, M. G.: Experimental masochism. *Arch Neurol Psychiat, 60:*402, 1948.

209. MASSERMAN, J. H.; LEVITT, M.; McAVOY, T.; KLING, A., and PECHTEL, C. T.: The cingulates and behavior. *J Nerv Ment Dis,* 126:148, 1958.

210. MASSERMAN, J. H.; LEVITT, M.; McAVOY, T.; KLING, A., and PECHTEL, C. T.: The amygdalae and behavior. *J Nerv Ment Dis.,* 126:14, 1958.

211. MASSERMAN, J. H., and PECHTEL, C. T.: Neuroses in monkeys: a preliminary report of experimental observations. *Ann NY Acad Sci, 56:*253, 1953.

212. MASSERMAN, J. H.; PECHTEL, C. T., and SCHREINER, L.: The role of olfaction in normal and neurotic behavior in animals. *Psychosom Med, 15:*396, 1953.

213. MASSERMAN, J. H., and PECHTEL, C. T.: The osmatic responses of normal and neurotic monkeys. *Ann NY Acad Sci, 58:*256, 1954.

214. MASSERMAN, J. H., and PECHTEL, C. T.: Differential effects of

cerebral lesions on susceptibility of animals to induction and relief of experimental neuroses. *Army Medical Service Research Progress Report,* 1st quarter, 1954, 433.

215. MASSERMAN, J. H., and PECHTEL, C. T.: How brain lesions affect normal and neurotic olfactory behavior in monkeys. *Trans Soc Biol Soc, 11*:256, 1956.

216. MASSERMAN, J. H., and PECHTEL, C. T.: Neurophysiologic and pharmacologic influence on experimental neuroses. *Amer J Psychiat, 113*:510, 1956.

217. MASSERMAN, J. H., and PECHTEL, C. T.: An experimental investigation of factors influencing drug action. *Psychiat Res Rep, 4*:126, 1956.

218. MASSERMAN, J. H., and PECHTEL, C. .T.: Cerebral localization: not where but in whom. *Amer J Psychiat, 116*:51, 1959.

219. MASSERMAN, J. H., and PECHTEL, C. T.: Penrod. Motion picture film. 16mm. Silent. Psychological Cinema Register, State University of Pa., Pa.

220. MASSERMAN, J. H., and RUBENFINE, R. L.: "Counting" behavior in cats. *J Gen Psychol., 30*:87, 1944.

221. MASSERMAN, J. H.; SCHREINER, L.; PECHTEL, C. T., and LEVITT, M.: Differential effects of lesions of the mediodorsal nuclei of the thalamus on normal and neurotic behavior in the cat. *J Nerv Ment Dis., 121*:26, 1955.

222. MASSERMAN, J. H., and SIEVER, P. W.: Dominance, neurosis and aggression. *Psychosom Med, 6*:87, 1944.

223. MASSERMAN, J. H.; WECHKIN, S., and TERRIS, W.: Altruistic behavior in rhesus monkeys. *Amer J Psychiat, 121*:584, 1964.

224. McCONNELL, J.: Transmission of training. *Med W News, 1*:4:47. 1960.

225. MEAD, MARGARET: *Male and Female.* New York, Morrow, 1949.

226. MEKLER, L. B.; LAPTEVA, N. N., and LOZOVSKII, D. V.: The extraction of toxic albumin from the serum of schizophrenic patients: a preliminary communication. *E H Neuropot., 58*:703-704, 1958.

227. MILLER, J. G.: Information input overload and psychopathology. *Amer J Psychiat, 116*:695, 1960.

228. MILLER, N. E.: Experiments in motivation. *Science, 126*:1276, 1957.

229. MILLER, N. E.: Chemical coding of behavior in the brain. *Science, 148*:328, 1965.

230. MIRSKY, A. F., and KATZ, M. S.: Avoidance "conditioning" in paramecia. *Science, 127*:1498, 1958.

231. MIRSKY, I. A.; MILLER, R. E., and MURPHY, J. V.: The communica-

tion of affect in rhesus monkeys. *J Amer Psychoanal Ass,* 6:433, 1958.

232. MISHLER, K. B., and COOGAN, J. P.: Do molecules remember? *Psychiat Rep,* 2:7, 1964.

233. MITTELMAN, B.: Psychodynamics of mobility. *Int J Psychoanal,* 39:1, 1958.

234. MOLES, A.: Acoustic behavior in animals. In R. G. Busnel (Ed.), *Animal Behavior.* Amsterdam, Elsevier, 1963. p. 125.

235. MONEY, J.; HAMPSON, L., and HAMPSON, K.: Quoted by Scott, J. P. Critical periods in behavior development. *Science, 138:* 949, 1962.

236. MONTAGU, M. F.: Man—and human nature. *Amer J Psychiat, 112:* 401, 1955.

237. MORGAN, C. L.: *Animal Life and Intelligence.* London, Arnold, 1891.

238. MORRIS, D.: The courtship dance of the swordtail. *Aquarest, 12,* March, 1955.

239. MORRIS, D.: The feather posture of birds and the problem of the origin of social signals. *Behavior, 9:6,* 1956.

240. MORRIS, G., *et al.*: Misconceptions and disorientation during sleep deprivation. *Arch Gen Psychiat (Chicago), 2:*247, 1960.

241. MOSCONA, A. A.: How cells associate. *Sci Amer, 206:*143, 1962.

242. MUELLER, H. J.: Genetic principles in human population. *Amer J Psychiat, 113:*481, 1956.

243. NAKAO, H.: Emotional behavior produced by hypothalamus stimulation. *Amer J Physiol, 194:*411-418, 1958.

244. NAUTA, W. J. W.: Central nervous organization and the endocrine motor system. In Nalbandoz, A. V. (Ed.), *Advances in Neuro-endocrinology.* Urbana, U. of Ill. 1963.

245. NORRIS, A. S.: Prenatal factors in intellectual and emotional development. *JAMA, 172:*413, 1960.

246. NOVEY, S.: The concept of the genital character. *Int J Psychoanal, 36:*90, 1955.

247. NUNBERG, H., and FEDERN, E.: *Minutes of the Vienna Psychoanalytic Society.* New York. Int Univs, 1960.

248. OLDS, J.: Self-stimulation of the brain. *Science, 127:*315-324, 1958.

249. O'NEAL, P., and ROBINS, L. N.: The relation of childhood behavior to adult psychiatric status. *Amer J Psychiat, 114:*961, 1958.

250. OPPENHEIMER, R.: Analogy in science. *Amer Psychol, 11:*127, 1956.

251. ORR, D. W.: Transference and countertransference. *J Amer Psychoanal Ass, 2:*83, 1954.

252. OSTOW, M.: The biologic bases of human behavior. In Arieti, S.

(Ed.), *American Handbook of Psychiatry*. New York, Basic Books, 1959, pp. 58-87.

253. OSTWALD, P. F.: Acoustic methods in psychiatry. *Sci Amer, 212*: 212-218, 1965.

254. OTTINGER, R.; DENENBERG, V. H., and STEPHENS, M. W.: Maternal emotionality, multiple mothering and emotionality in maturity. *J Comp Physiol Psychol, 56*:313-317, 1963.

255. PAPEZ, T. W.: A proposed mechanism of emotion. *Arch Neurol Psychiat, 38*:725, 1937.

256. PASAMANICK, B., and LILIENFIELD, A.: Association of maternal and fetal factors with development of mental deficiency. *JAMA, 159*: 155, 1955.

257. PATTIE, F. A.: The gregarious behavior of normal chicks and chicks hatched in isolation. *J Comp Psychol, 21*:161, 1936.

258. PAULING, L.: Genetic and somatic effects of C^{14}. *Science, 128*:1183, 1958.

259. PAULING, L.: The molecular basis of genetics. *Amer J Psychiat, 113*:492, 1956.

260. PAVLOV, I. P.: *Lectures on Conditioned Reflexes*. New York, Int Pubs, 1928, p. 242.

261. PECHTEL, C.; McAVOY, T.; LEVITT, M.; KLING, A., and MASSERMAN, J. H.: The cingulates and behavior. *J Nerv Ment Dis, 126*: 148-152, 1958.

262. PENFIELD, W., and MILLER, B.: The interpretive cortex. *Science, 159*:1722, 1959.

263. PENFIELD, W., and MILLER, B.: Cortex and memory. *Arch Neurol Psychiat, 79*:475, 1958.

264. PIAGET, J.: The child in modern physics. *Sci Amer, 196*:46, 1957.

265. PRIBRAM, K.: Freud's project. In Greenfield, N.S., and Lewis, W.C. (Eds.), *Psychoanalysis and Current Biological Thought*. Madison, U. of Wis., 1965. pp. 81-92.

266. PUMPIAN-MINDLIN, E.: Changing concepts of therapy in a veterans administration mental hygiene clinic. *Amer J Psychiat, 113*: 1095, 1947.

267. PUMPIAN-MINDLIN, E. (Ed.): *Psychoanalysis as Science*. Palo Alto, Stanford, 1953.

268. RADO, S., and DANIELS, G. E.: *Changing Concepts in Psychoanalytic Medicine*. New York, Grune, 1956.

269. RAINER, J. D.: The concept of mind in the framework of genetics. In J. Scher (Ed.), *Theories of Mind*. New York, Blakiston, 1962.

270. RAZRAN, G.: Pavlov and Lamarck. *Science, 128*:758, 1958.

271. RELTER, J., JR.: Defense of mate and mating chamber in a wood roach. *Science, 143*:1459, 1964.
272. RENSCH, B.: The intelligence of elephants. *Sci Amer, 196*:44, 1957.
273. RESSLER, R. H.: Parental handling in two strains of mice reared by foster parents. *Science, 137*:129-130, 1962.
274. RICHTER, C. P.: On the phenomenon of sudden death in animals and man. *Psychosom Med, 19*:191, 1957.
275. RIOCH, D. McK.: Certain aspects of "conscious" phenomenon and their neural correlates. *Amer J Psychiat, 111*:810, 1955.
276. ROBERTS, W.: Both rewarding and punishing effects from stimulation of posterior hypothalamus of cats with same electrode at same intensity. *J Comp Physiol Psychol, 51*:4, 1958.
277. ROBERTS, W.: Rapid escape learning without avoidance learning motivated by hypothalamic stimulation in cats. *J Comp Physiol Psychol, 51*:391, 1958.
278. ROSVOLD, H. E.: The effects of electroconvulsive shocks on gestation and maternal behavior. I. *J Comp Physiol Psychol, 42*:118, 1949; II *42*:207, 1949.
279. RULE, C.: A biologically based theory of human behavior. *Amer J Psychiat, 121*:344, 1964.
280. RUSSELL, B.: *An Outline of Philosophy.* London, Allen and Unwin, 1927.
281. SALZMAN, L.: Masochism. In J. H. Masserman (Ed.), *Science and Psychoanalysis.* New York, Grune, vol. II, 1959.
282. SAUER, E. G. F.: Celestial navigation in birds. *Sci Amer, 199*:42, 1958.
283. SCHIFF, W.; COVINESS, J. A., and GIBSON, J. J.: Pesistent fear responses in rhesus monkeys to the optical stimulus of "looming." *Science, 136*:982, 1962.
284. SCHILLER, C.: *Instinctive Behavior.* New York, Int Univ, 1957.
285. SCHLESINGER, B.: *Higher Cerebral Functions and Their Clinical Disorders.* New York, Grune, p. 39 ff.
286. SCHNEIRLA, T. C.: Learning and orientation in ants. *Comp Psychol Monogr, 6*:139, 1929.
287. SCHALLER, G.: *The Mountain Gorilla.* Chicago, U. of Chicago, 1963.
288. SCOTT, J. P.: *The Process of Socialization in Higher Animals.* New York, Milbank Fund Publications, 1953.
289. SCOTT, J. P.: Critical periods in behavior development. *Science, 138*:949, 1962.
290. SCOTT, W. E.: Data on song in birds. *Science, 14*:522, 1901.
291. SCULL, C.; NANCE, M., and ROLL, G. F.: Research in the Soviet Union. *JAMA, 167*:2120, 1958.

292. SEBEOK, T. A.: Animal communication. *Science, 147*:1906, 1965.
293. SEITZ, P. F. D.: The effects of infantile experiences upon adult behavior in animal subjects. I. Effects of litter size during infancy upon adult behavior in the rat. *Amer J Psychiat, 110*:916, 1954.
294. SHEER, D. E. (Ed.): *Electrical Stimulation of the Brain.* Austin, U. of Texas, 1961.
295. SHERRINGTON, C. S.: The spinal cord. Quoted in J. F. Fulton, *Psysiology of the Nervous System.* New York, Oxford U. P., 1938, pp. 125, 215.
296. SHURLEY, J.: Profound experimental sensory isolation. *Amer J Psychiat, 117*:539, 1960.
297. SIBOL, J.: The strangest birds in the world. *Life,* March 25, 1957, p. 88.
298. SMART, R. G.: Effects of alcohol on conflict and avoidance behavior. *Quart J Stud Alcohol, 26*:127-205, 1965.
299. SIMPSON, G. G.: *The Meaning of Evolution.* New Haven, Yale, 1949.
300. SMITH, K.: Pattern vision and visual acuity. *Gen Psychiat, 53*:251-272, 1938.
301. SMITH, F. L.; SIMON, A., and LINGOES, J. C.: Excretion of urinary corticoids in mental patients. *J Nerv Ment Dis, 124*:381, 1956.
302. SONTAG, L. W.: The significance of fetal environmental differences. *Amer J Obstet Gynec, 42*:196-1003, 1941.
303. SPERRY, R. W.: Cerebral organization and behavior. *Science, 133*: 1749, 1961.
304. SPIEGEL, E. A.; WYCIS, H. T.; ORCHINIK, C., and FREED, A.: A follow-up study of patients treated by thalamotomy and by combined frontal and thalamic lesions. *J Nerv Ment Dis, 124*:399-404, 1956.
305. SPIEGEL, E. A.; WYCIS, H. T.; ORCHINIK, C., and FREED, A.: Thalamic chronotaraxis. *Amer J Psychiat, 113*:97, 1956.
306. SPITZ, R. A.: Infantile depression. In Hoch, P., and Zubin, J. (Eds.), *Depression.* New York, Grune, 1954.
307. STERN, A.: Science and the philosopher. *Sci Amer, 44*:281, 1956.
308. STONE, L.: Brief psychotherapy. *Psychoanal Quart, 20*:215, 1951.
309. STOTT, D. H.: Physical and mental handicaps following disturbed pregnancy. *Lancet, 1*:1006, 1957.
310. STRUPP, H. H.: The psychotherapist's contribution to the treatment process. *Behav Sci, 3*:34, 1958.
311. SZASZ, T. S.: On the psychoanalytic theory of instincts. *Psychoanal Quart, 21*:25, 1952.
312. SZASZ, T. S.: The libido theory. *Ann NY Acad Sci, 76*:975, 1959.

313. SZYMANSKI, J. S.: Modification of the innate behavior of cockroaches. *J Anim Behav, 2*:81, 1912.

314. THIESSEN, D. D., and ROGERS, D. A.: Endocrine effects of overcrowding. *Psychol Bull, 58*:449, 1961.

315. THOMPSON, W. R.: Influence of prenatal maternal anxiety on emotionality in young rats. *Science, 125*:698, 1957.

316. THOMPSON, W. R., and HERON, W.: Maternal influences. *Canad J Psychol, 8*:17, 1954.

317. THOMPSON, W. R., and MELZOCK, R.: "Whirling" behavior in dogs as related to early experience. *Science, 123*:939, 1956.

318. THORPE, W. H.: *Learning and Instinct in Animals.* London, Methueix, 1956.

319. TINBERGEN, N.: *The Study of Instinct.* London, Oxford U. P., 1951.

320. TOLMAN, E. C.: *Purposive Behavior in Animals and Men.* New York, Century, 1951.

321. TOMPKINS, S.: The psychology of being right—and left. *Trans Wash U,* Nov.-Dec., 1965.

322. TOYNBEE, A. J.: *A Study of History* (Abridged by D. C. Somervell). New York, Oxford U. P., 1957.

323. TREVARIHEN, C. B.: Double visual learning in split-brain monkeys. *Science, 136*:258, 1962.

324. VERNON, J., and HOFFMAN, J.: Effects of sensory deprivation. *Science, 123*:1074, 1956.

325. VEXHALL, J. VON.: *Umwelt und Innenwelt der Tiere.* Berlin, Springer, 1920.

326. WAISMANN, H. A., and HARLOW, H. F.: Experimental phenylketonuria in monkeys. *Science, 147*:605, 1965.

327. WAKEMAN, B. H., and ADAMS, R. H.: Brain function. *J Neuropath Exp Neurol, 15*:293, 1956.

328. WALD, G.: The significance of vertebrate metamorphosis. *Science, 128*:1481, 1958.

329. WARDEN, C. J.; JENKINS, T. N., and WARNER, L. H.: *Introduction to Comparative Psychology.* New York, Ronald, 1934.

330. WATSON, R. E.: Experimentally induced conflict in cats. *Psychosom Med, 16*:341, 1954.

331. WEST, L. J., and GLASS, A. J.: Sexual behavior and the military law. In R. Slovenko (Ed.), *Sexual Behavior and the Law.* Springfield, Thomas, 1965.

332. WHEELIS, A.: The vocational hazards of psychoanalysis. *Int J Psa, 37*:171, 1956.

333. WHITEHEAD, A. N.: *Science and the Modern World.* New York, Mentor, 1925.

334. WHORF, B. L.: *Language, Thought and Reality.* Cambridge, M.I. 1956.

335. WIENER, N.: Some maxims for biologists and psychologists. *Dialectica, 4*:3, 1950.

336. WIESNER, B. P., and SHEARD, N. M.: *Maternal Behavior in the Rat.* Edinburgh, Oliver and Boyd, 1933.

337. WOLF, K. M.: Child imprinting. *Genet Psychol Monogr, 34*:57-125, 1946.

338. WOLFF, H. S.: Life stress and bodily disease: a formulation. In *Proc Ass Res Nerv Ment Dis,* Baltimore, Williams & Wilkins, 1950. *Gen Psychiat (Chicago), 4*:395, 1961.

339. WOLPE, J.: *Psychotherapy by Reciprocal Inhibition.* Palo Alto, Stanford, 1958.

340. WYNNE-EDWARDS, V. C.: *Animal Dispersion in Relation to Social Behavior.* New York, Hafner, 1962, p. 16.

341. WYNNE-EDWARDS, V. C.: Self-regulating systems in populations of animals. *Science, 147*:1543, 1965.

342. YERKES, R. M.: *Chimpanzees, a Laboratory Colony.* New Haven, Yale, 1943.

343. YOUWILER, A., *et al.*: Serum oxidase tests and schizophrenia. *Arch Gen Psychia (Chicago), 4*:395, 1961.

344. ZAJONC, R. B.: Social facilitation. *Science, 149*:269-274, 1965.

345. ZUCKERMAN, S.: *The Social Life of Monkeys and Apes.* London, Kegan Paul, Trench, Trunmer, 1932.

The author wishes to thank W. B. Saunders Co., Grune & Stratton, Inc., and Basic Books, Inc. for permission to modify and reassemble previous writings by the author published under their respective auspices.

NAME INDEX

A

Allee, W. C., 33
Angyal, A., 9
Arbit, J., 11

B

Bailey, P., 9
Barnett, L., 85, 86
Bayer, L., 50
Beach, F. A., 82
Best, J. B., 33, 54
Berzelius, J. J., 14
Bobbit, Ruth, 45
Bonner, J. T., 47
Bourne, E., 25
Bowlby, J., 45, 63
Boycott, B. B., 17
Brady, J., 9, 69
Brandt, Leonore, 44
Bronowski, J., 87
Brown, F., 16
Bucy, P., 34
Burton, M., 32, 36, 48, 49, 82
Butler, R. A., 28
Bykov, K. M., 69

C

Calhoun, J. B., 46
Cameron, D. E., 17
Chapman, L., 27
Chen, S. C., 50
Christian, J. J., 20
Clark, L. D., 49
Cleghorn, R. H., 13
Cobb, S., 9
Colby, K. M., 6
Commoner, B., 15
Conger, J. V., 78
Conradi, E., 23
Coogan, L., 17

Cope, C. L., 13
Craig, W., 35, 40

D

Darlington, D. C., 20
Davis, L., 25
Delgado, J. M. R., 9
Dement, W., 26
Denenberg, V. H., 40, 41
Deutsch, J. S., 9
Dobie, J. R., 28

E

Edwardes, A., 37, 38
Eibl-Eibesfeldt, I., 49
Einstein, A., 87, 89
Eysenck, H. J., 64

F

Fairbanks, L., 27
Ferster, C. B., 29
Fischberg, M., 15
Fisher, A. E., 34
Friedman, C., 25
Freed, E. X., 78
French, J. W., 54
Freud, S., 3, 4, 6, 21, 49, 59, 86
Frings, H., 23
Fry, A., 39

G

Gantt, W. H., 19, 52, 54, 62
Gerard, R., 9
Gelber, S., 17
Gibbons, J. L., 13
Gillard, E. T., 31
Ginsberg, B., 14, 15, 63
Glass, B., 39, 88
Godel, A. W., 86

SUBJECT INDEX

A

Adaptation, 53
  developmental influences on,
    57-59
  failures, vi
Affection, 25
  cross-species fixations of, 43-45
  and clinging, 45
Aggression, 49-50, 59-61
  displaced, 59
  primal, 4
Altruism
  simian, 23, 48
Amphioxus, vii, 52
Animal studies
  species used in, 54
Animal warfare, 49-50
Anthropomorphism, vii, 51
Anxiety
  pervasive, 65
  primal
    Ur-defenses against, 84, 87

B

Behavior
  esthetic, in animals, 28-29
  parental, 40-46
    hormonal influences on, 40
    mating and, 41
    ontogenic factors in, 41-42
    overpopulation on, effects of,
      45-46
    patterns of, 42-43
  sexual, 32-39
    biologic purpose of, 32
    cultural factors in, 37-39
    uxorial patterns in, 36-37
  social
    species-characteristic, 47-49
Biodynamic principles, 53-54 (See
    also Adaptation; Motivation;

Neurotigenesis; Versatility)
Biodynamic therapies (See
    Neurosis, experimental)
Bioevolutionary factors
  importance of, 3
Birds (See also Communications;
    Instinct)
  celestial navigation in, 18
Brain
  ablation, 10
  centers, 9-12
  electrical stimulation of, 9-10
  lesions, 10

C

Collaboration (See Social
    collaboration)
Communication
  animal, vii
  in baboons, 23-24
  in birds, 23
  in monkeys, 23
  interspecies, 24
  modes of, 22-25
Complex
  Oedipus, v
Conflict
  adaptational, 62-64
  approach-approach, 63-64
Contrectation, 35-36
Coordinates, distortion of (See
    Feedback, delayed)
Crossbreeding, 40-41
Cross-species friendships, 48-49

D

Deprivation, 57
  sensory, 25
Displacement, 59-60
Drives, 11-12 (See also
    Motivation)